Tales from Far and Near

Edited by

Arthur Guy Terry

Associate Professor of History

Northwestern University

History Stories of Other Lands

10 09 08 07

List of Stories

1

The Story of a Wooden Horse

VERY long ago, an old blind man, named Homer, sang songs to the people of Greece. He told stories in his songs, and other men wrote down some of them in books. The tale of the Wooden Horse is one of these stories.

There was once a long war, which lasted for ten years. Some men of the land of Greece were fighting against the people of the city of Troy.

The Greeks sailed in their ships to Troy. But they could not get into the city, for the gates were shut. So they put up tents and built huts on the plains outside the city walls, and they waited there.

Sometimes the men of Troy rushed out of

the city and tried to drive the Greeks away. But they could not do this. Sometimes the Greeks tried to break down the gates or climb the high walls of the city. But they too failed.

At the end of ten years, the Greeks began to grow tired of the long fight. They wanted to go back to their homes, but they did not like to leave without first taking the city.

At last, one of the leaders found a way to do this. He made the Greeks build a large horse of wood. The horse was hollow inside, and it was so large that it could hold twelve men. It was moved upon wheels.

This great horse was set up on the plain in front of the city. In the dark of night, twelve brave Greeks got inside it, while the rest of the Greeks sailed away in their ships. But the ships did not go far; they stopped a little way off, where they could not be seen.

When daylight came, the men of Troy looked down at the plain. No Greeks were to be seen. Full of surprise they crowded out of the city, and on the plain they found the big

Dragging the wooden horse

horse of wood. They did not know that twelve Greeks were hidden inside it.

They looked at it, and they touched it. They walked all round it, and one or two of the most daring among them threw their spears at it. But they could make nothing of it. All they could think was that the Greeks might come back some day and that they had left the horse there for luck.

Some men of Troy wanted to burn it, but most of them wanted to keep it. They said that if they could only get this huge wooden horse inside their city wall, then luck would be with them and not with the Greeks.

They dragged the horse on its wheels into the city. At night, when it was dark, the Greeks came from their hiding-place and opened the gates of Troy. By this time, the other Greeks had sailed back again. When they saw the gates open, they rushed into the city, burned the houses, and killed many of the people.

That was the end of the great war, which lasted for ten long years.

2

Romulus and Remus

ONCE upon a time, long, long ago, two baby boys were born in Italy. These babies were twins, and their names were Romulus and Remus. Their grandfather was a king, but he had been driven from his kingdom by his brother.

The brother, who did this unfair thing, took the crown and made himself king.

He was not a good man. When he heard of the twin babies, he was afraid.

"If these little princes grow big and strong," he said to himself, "they may kill me some day and give the crown back to their grandfather."

So he sent some of his men to take the babies

and to throw them into the river. This cruel thing was done. The men put the poor little babies into a basket and threw it into the river. Then they went and told the new king that the babies were drowned.

But this was not true. The basket floated on the water and was carried down the stream. Then it was washed to the bank of the river and left there. And so they were saved.

But they were cold and hungry, and they

cried loudly as they lay in the basket near the river.

It is said that a kind mother-wolf heard the cries of the babies and came to them. She carried them away from the river to a nice dry place under a wild fig tree. She warmed them under her shaggy coat and fed them with her own milk.

This she did every day until they grew so big that they could eat other food. Then, it is said, a big woodpecker came every day with meat in her beak for them. And in this way the twins grew strong.

After a time, one of the new king's shepherds passed by and saw the babies. He did not know who they were, but, as he was a kind man, he took them to his cottage and asked his wife to take care of them.

The two young princes lived in the shepherd's hut until they were big strong boys. They played with his children, helped to watch the sheep upon the hillside, and were quite happy. But they did not know they were princes. Years were to pass before they found out.

The new king's sheep fed upon the grass on one part of the hills, and the old king's sheep fed upon the grass on another part of the hills. Sometimes there were fights between the new king's shepherds and the old king's shepherds.

In one of these fights, the shepherds of the old king caught Remus and took him away to the house of their master. Romulus ran after his brother to try to help him, but the shepherds got him also. Then the two lads

The old king and his grandsons

were taken before the old king, who was their grandfather.

When the old king saw the tall pretty boys in their plain clothes, he stared.

"Surely those fine lads are not the sons of a shepherd?" said he.

He asked many things of the boys and of the shepherds. Then he sent for the shepherd who had cared for them all these years, and from him he learned their strange story. So the old king found out that the boys were indeed his grandsons, and he was very happy.

He told Romulus and Remus that they were princes and that the new king had tried to drown them when they were babies. This story made the lads very angry. They went to the new king's palace and killed him. Then they gave the crown back to their grandfather.

But they would not stay with the old king.

"No," said they, "we will build a city for ourselves near the river where we were saved." And they went back to that place.

"Let us build our city here!" said Romulus, pointing to one hilltop.

"No, let us build it here!" said Remus, pointing to another hilltop.

And they could not agree.

Then they said: "We will watch the sky, and the one of us who first sees a flock of birds flying past shall build the city where he pleases."

So Romulus watched the sky from one hilltop, and Remus watched it from another. Remus first saw a flock of birds fly past. He saw six; but, soon afterwards, Romulus saw twelve birds.

"It is for me to build the city, for I saw the birds first," said Remus.

"No! It is for me to build it, for I saw more birds than you," said Romulus. So they could not agree.

At first, the brothers spoke angrily to one another. Then they began to fight; and in the fight poor Remus was killed.

So it was Romulus who built the city. He

called it Rome after his own name.

We do not know that this story is true. The old books, which told of it, are lost. But one thing is quite true. The city of Rome still stands upon the hills near a river in Italy.

3

The Keeping of the Bridge

ONE day, long years ago, there was a great stir at Rome. Upon the dusty roads outside the city, crowds of people were running or walking very fast. Now and then, some of these people looked back, as if they feared that danger was coming behind them.

There were young men and women, old men and women, boys and girls, and babies. There were sick people who could not walk and had to be carried by their servants. And there were workmen from the fields with their spades and reaping hooks in their hands.

There were beasts too; sheep and goats, cows, donkeys, and mules. There were many carts loaded with corn and food, and with tables, chairs, and beds. All these people, and beasts, and carts were going in haste to Rome. And this is why.

Behind them, over the green fields and

A great army was coming along the road.

along the dusty roads, a great army was coming. There were thousands of foot soldiers and thousands of horse soldiers in that army. They meant to fight the people of Rome and to take their city.

These soldiers burned the houses of the country people and broke their fences; they trod down their corn and stole their food and their goods. No wonder the poor people ran away as fast as they could to Rome. They hoped to be safe inside the strong walls of the city, with the gates shut.

When the wise men of Rome heard the story of the people who crowded in at their gates, they went quickly to the top of the high wall and looked out over the river.

Upon the other side of the river, they saw a cloud of dust. This cloud of dust came nearer every moment. It was stirred up by the feet of all the soldiers and horses marching rapidly toward Rome.

There was a wooden bridge over the river. The army would have to cross this bridge to reach the city.

"We must break down the bridge," cried one of the wise men. "Then our foes will be stopped, and Rome will be saved."

The Roman soldiers ran out of the city with

axes in their hands and began to cut down the bridge. But it was too late. The great army was already near, and there was not time to cut through the thick posts and planks.

"Rome will be lost!" cried one of the men; and the women wept. But there was a very brave man in Rome named Horatius. This man now stood out of the crowd and shouted loudly: "Rome shall be saved! Cut down the bridge quickly! I will stop the army, if two other men will help me."

There were many other brave men in the city.

"I will help you!" cried one of these.

"And I!" cried another.

So Horatius and the other two men walked over the bridge and stood side by side near the far end. Behind them, their friends cut fast at the bridge with their axes, to break it down.

When the thousands of the enemy saw the three brave Romans waiting for them on the bridge, they stopped in surprise. "How can three men stop an army?" they cried, and they laughed aloud. Then they rushed on.

But the bridge was not wide. Not more than three or four men could enter it at once. When the first three soldiers came on, they were cut down and killed by Horatius and his friends; and so were the next and the next.

The great army on the river bank shouted with anger. But the Romans on the other side of the river shouted with joy.

Horatius jumped into the river.

The bridge was nearly down. Already there was a large gap in it. Very soon the last timbers would fall.

"Come back!" cried the Romans to their three brave friends. "Jump over the gap before it is too wide!"

The two brave men who stood beside Horatius jumped quickly. They were safe. But Horatius did not leave his post.

"I will not come until the last plank is down," cried he.

So the Romans cut faster and faster with their axes. On came the soldiers again. But now the last piece of wood had fallen into the water. The bridge was down, and Rome was safe.

Then brave Horatius turned back and jumped into the rushing water. All men feared that he would be drowned, but he swam across the river and landed safe in Rome again.

The Romans did all they could to honor these three brave men who saved their city.

They wrote their story in books, so that all people might read of the good thing that they did.

4

Alexander the Great and His Horse

ONE of the most famous of the Greeks was a Macedonian named Alexander the Great, who made himself master of a large part of the world. He had a splendid horse, which he always rode when he went to battle. He won this horse when he was a boy, by his wisdom and boldness.

This is how he won it. The horse was sent as a present to King Philip, father of the young prince Alexander. The king went to a wide plain to try it, and his son and all his great men went with him.

But it was soon found that the horse was very wild. It kicked and reared so that no man could mount its back. The king was angry that so wild an animal should be sent to him and gave orders for it to be taken back at once.

The prince was vexed to hear this. "It is a pity to lose such a fine horse, because no man is brave enough to mount it," said he.

The king thought his son spoke without thinking.

"Your words are bold," said he, "but are you bold enough to mount the horse yourself?"

The young prince went up to the restless animal. He took the bridle and turned its

Alexander riding Bucephalus

head toward the sun. He did so, because he had seen that the horse was afraid of its own black shadow, which kept moving upon the ground before its eyes.

Alexander the Great

With its face to the sun, the horse could no longer see the shadow, which now fell on the ground behind it. It soon became quiet. Then the prince stroked it and patted it gently, and, by and by, he sprang quickly upon its back.

The horse at once set off at a gallop over the plain, with the boy bravely holding on. The king and his men were in great fear, for they thought the prince would be thrown to the ground and killed. But they need not have been afraid.

Soon the horse grew tired of its gallop and began to trot. Then Alexander turned and gently rode it back. The men shouted, and the king took his son in his arms and shed tears of joy.

The horse was given to the young prince. It loved its master and would kneel down for him to mount, but it would let no other person get upon its back.

The books tell us that at last, after many years, it was hurt in a fight. But it carried its master to a safe place. Then it lay down and died.

Alexander built a city at that place and gave the city the horse's name, Bucephalus.

5

Alexander Visits Diogenes

WHEN this little prince who tamed the wild horse grew up, he became a great king. He owned many lands and ruled over many people. One day this king, who was now called Alexander the Great, decided to pay a visit to some of the larger cities of Greece. Among the cities that he planned to visit was the City of Corinth.

When the people of Corinth heard that King Alexander was coming to their city, they were very much pleased. All went out to see him. Everybody, even the leading men of the city, went outside the walls to meet the king and to praise him. But there was one man in Corinth who did not go. That man was Diogenes.

Alexander at the home of Diogenes

Now, Diogenes was the wisest man in all Corinth. Indeed, he was one of the wisest men who ever lived. He was so wise that even while he lived he had become very famous. Men came from far lands and distant cities to see him and to hear what he had to say.

Diogenes did not believe many things that most people in those times believed. He did many things that we today should call very queer. He thought it was wrong for any person to have more than was needed. He also believed that no man needs very much. For that reason, Diogenes lived in a big barrel instead of a house. When he became tired of living in one place, all he had to do was roll his barrel along until he came to another place that he did like. There he stayed until he felt ready to move again. Strangest of all, this queer man liked to spend his time sitting in the sun and talking to those who were about him.

It is said that one day at noontime, when the sun was shining brightly, Diogenes was seen walking through the streets of Corinth with a lighted lantern and looking from side to side, as if he were hunting for something.

Someone who saw him asked, "Why do you carry a lantern when the sun is shining?"

"I am looking for an honest man," answered Diogenes.

Now Alexander had heard about Diogenes and his wise sayings. The great king wanted to see him. In fact, Diogenes was the only man in all Corinth whom he really cared about seeing at all. For that reason, the king was disappointed when he saw that Diogenes was not among those who had come out from the city to greet him.

But Alexander decided that he would see the wise man. So he said that if Diogenes would not come to see the king, then the king would go to see Diogenes. He asked to be taken to Diogenes's home. Some citizens led Alexander to an out-of-the-way place. There the king found the old man lying on the ground beside his barrel, enjoying the warmth and light of the sun.

Just then Diogenes saw that the king and a great party of people were coming toward him. He sat up and looked about him.

Alexander drew quite near and, after greeting the old man, he said: "Diogenes, I have heard a great deal about you and your wisdom. Is there anything that I can do for you?"

"Yes," said Diogenes, "you can stand aside a little, so as not to keep the sunshine from me."

This answer was, of course, very different from the one which the king expected, so he was much surprised. But the strange answer did not make him angry. Indeed, it only made him admire Diogenes all the more.

As he rode away, he said to one of his soldiers, "If I were not Alexander, I should like to be Diogenes."

6
King Arthur

LONG ago, a baby boy was born in England, and his name was Arthur. This baby was a prince, for his father was a king.

A wise old man, called Merlin, took baby Arthur away from his father and mother for safety. He carried him to the castle of a good and true lord, whose name was Sir Ector.

Merlin told the king and queen it was best to do this. And they let him do as he wished, because he was very wise. No other person knew that a prince had been born, for it was a secret. Sir Ector was kind to the young prince, and Arthur thought the good lord was indeed his father.

After a time, the king fell sick. He called

his lords to his bedside and told them to put the crown on Prince Arthur's head and make him king. Then he died.

But the lords did not do as the king said. They did not know that there was a prince at Sir Ector's castle. So there was trouble in the land, for first one great lord and then another tried to take the crown for himself.

Then wise old Merlin called the lords to come to a great church; and they did so. When the lords left the church, they saw a large square stone upon the ground outside. A fine sword was stuck into this stone, and round about the point of the sword were some words written in gold letters.

This is what they said: "Who pulls this sword from the stone is the king."

What a strange thing! The lords were full of wonder. First one lord and then another tried to pull out the sword, but not one of them could move it.

Then many other men came to see the stone. Every man tried to draw out the sword,

but not one could do so. Sir Ector came with the rest, and also his son, and the young prince Arthur.

Sir Ector and his son could not lift the sword, but Arthur pulled it out of the stone quite easily.

All men wondered to see a young lad do this thing, which strong men could not do.

"Arthur is our king!" cried some of them.

But others said: "We will not let Sir Ector's son rule over us. He is not a prince."

Then up stood Merlin and spoke. "Arthur is your king," said he. "He is a prince, for he is the son of your last king."

The people were glad when they heard the words of the wise old man.

"Arthur is our king!" they shouted.

And the crown was put on the young prince's head.

Arthur grew up to be a brave and good king. He fought and won many fights, but at last there came a day when he was beaten.

All but one of his brave lords were killed in that fight, and the king was sorely hurt. He lay on the ground, and the lord who was left alive wept beside him.

Then the king knew in his heart the things that must be done.

"Take my sword to the waterside and throw it into the water," said he. "Then come back and tell me what you see."

So the lord took the sword to the waterside. But, as he held it in his hand, he saw shining gems upon the hilt. He could not bear to throw away so fine a thing, so he hid it under a tree. But he told the king he had thrown it into the water.

"What did you see there?" asked King Arthur.

"I saw only the waves and winds," said the lord.

"That is not true," said the king sternly, for he knew in his heart what things must happen.

He sent the lord once more to the waterside. And once more the lord hid the sword and told the king he had thrown it into the water.

"What did you see there?" asked King Arthur again.

"I saw only the waves stirred by the wind," said the lord.

Then the king was very angry. "That is not true," said he. "If you do not now do what I have told you, I will rise and kill you."

So the lord went once more to the waterside. This time he did not look at the shining gems and threw the sword far out over the water.

A hand rose from the waves and took the sword. Three times it shook the sword and then drew it down into the water. So the lord went back to the king and told him all he had seen.

"Carry me to the waterside," said King Arthur. The lord did so, and there, close to the bank, he found a barge with many fair ladies on it.

"Put me on the barge," said the king. So the lord laid him gently on the barge. And three fair ladies, who were queens, bent over the king and took care of him.

Then the barge moved slowly away from the land.

"Ah! my master! What shall I do without

you?" cried the lord.

"Comfort yourself, and do well," said the king. "I go to a green island to be healed of my hurt."

Slowly the barge moved away, until the lord could see it no more. Then he went into the forest, weeping sadly, for he loved his master the king.

7

King Alfred's Dream

ONCE upon a time the good king, Alfred the Great, was in sad trouble. His strong foes, the Danes, had come over the sea in ships to England. They had killed many English people and burned their houses.

Alfred and his men fought bravely, but they were beaten. The Danes drove them this way and that way. At last, the king hid himself, with a few of his friends, in a poor little hut in a lonely place. The weather was very cold, and they had little to eat.

One day the king's friends went out to look for food, while King Alfred stayed at home. He was very sad and lonely, so he took his Bible and began to read.

By and by, a poor man came to the door. He was cold and hungry.

"Will you give me a morsel of food for Christ's sake?" asked he.

There was one loaf in the hut and a little wine in a jug. That was all. But the king gave these to the beggar, and the poor man was very thankful.

When he had gone away, the king took his book again and went on reading. After a time, he fell asleep and dreamed a strange dream.

He dreamed that an angel stood beside him in the hut, and the angel's face was the face of the poor beggar. The angel told the king that it was indeed he who had asked for food.

He said also that God had seen the sad trouble of the king and his people and would soon help them to drive away their foes.

When King Alfred awoke, he did not forget his dream. He felt sure it was a message from heaven.

By and by, his friends came back with a

great many fish, which they had caught. The king told them of the coming of the poor man and of his own dream.

One of Alfred's battleships

They were happy to hear of these things. Soon they set to work to call the English soldiers together again, and King Alfred led them to battle once more.

This time the English beat the Danes. So the king's dream came true.

8

King Canute on the Seashore

ABOUT a hundred years after the death of King Alfred, the English were ruled by a king named Canute. He was a strong king who ruled his country well and won many battles over the fierce people round about him.

Canute became such a great leader that those near him were always praising his strength and courage. They told him that he was the bravest and greatest man alive and that everything in the world would obey his orders.

The king was a man of good sense. He knew that he was strong and brave, and he tried to rule his kingdom well. But he also knew that he was only a man and that many things were not under his control. Therefore, he grew very tired of the praise, which his foolish officers and chiefs heaped upon him, and he sought some method of teaching them a lesson.

One day the leaders of the kingdom were encamped by the seashore. The officers were praising the king, as was their habit. King Canute saw that the chance had now come to show them how foolish they were.

The king ordered his men to place his throne on the beach close by the edge of the water. Then he asked: "Is there any man in the world as mighty as I?"

Quickly the king's men replied, "There is no one in all the world who can compare with you."

"Will all things obey my command?"

"Nothing will dare to disobey you, O king," they said. "The whole world gives you honor and bows before you."

Then the king looked down at the little

King Canute commanding the sea

waves, which were washing the sand at his feet, and questioned his men again:

"Will the sea obey me?"

The officers looked at one another, but they did not know what to say or what to do. Although they did not quite believe that the sea would obey the king, they were afraid to tell him that. Finally the king repeated his question. Then the men had to answer.

"Command the sea, O king," they said, "and it will obey."

Then the king cried: "Water, I command you to come no farther! Stay back, and do not dare to touch my feet!"

But since not even a king can command the sea, the tide came in just as it had always done. The water rose higher and higher. It reached the king's feet. Then it reached his knees. At last, it came up about his waist. His officers stood about him, afraid. They thought that their king must be mad.

At last, Canute stood up, took his crown from his head, and turned to his officers. "Let everyone here," he said, "learn from what he has just seen. No man, however strong, can hope to rule the sea. There is only one King who has all power. It is He who rules the sea and the land, the sun and the stars. You should serve Him, praise Him, and obey His commands before all others."

9

The Little Soldiers of the Cross

At one time, men thought that the best thing to do was to fight. Nearly every man was a soldier, and there were many wars and battles.

Children like to do as grown-up people do. The boys and girls of those days liked nothing so much as playing at soldiers and battles and fighting with one another.

For many years, there was a war called the War of the Cross, or the Crusades. From many countries, men went to fight in the Holy Land.

The city where Christ died on the Cross is in the Holy Land. The people who lived and ruled there did not love and serve Him. So

Christian men thought it would be a good and noble thing to take Jerusalem from them. That is what men fought for in the War of the Cross.

Soldiers who went to this war were called Soldiers of the Cross. Each of them wore a cross upon his coat or cloak.

The children saw their fathers and brothers set out for the Holy Land and heard a great deal about the long journey over land and sea to Jerusalem. Then they made crosses of paper or of cloth, put them upon their own clothing, and played at being little Soldiers

A view of Jerusalem

of the Cross.

After a time, some of the bigger boys began to think it would be a better thing to go to the War of the Cross and fight for Jerusalem than to play at doing so.

I am sorry to say that a few of the preachers told them this. They said that the children's weak little arms would be made strong if they were real Soldiers of the Cross. They told them, too, that a dry pathway to the Holy Land would be opened through the sea for them.

A shepherd boy in France heard these things and thought it was his duty to lead an army of children to Jerusalem. He rode in a grand car about the country, calling on the children to follow him.

From all parts of the land, thousands of boys, and even a few girls, trooped after the car. They were eager to see new lands and to be real soldiers as their fathers and brothers were.

The parents of the children begged them to

stay at home. "The way to the Holy Land is too long and too hard for little feet," said they.

But the boys and girls paid no heed to their words.

"We are going to Jerusalem," they cried, and they ran after the shepherd boy, dancing and singing merrily as they went.

Alas! They never reached the end of that journey. The way was indeed long and hard. At every town, the children asked, "Is this Jerusalem?" They did not know how far they had to go.

The little ones soon became tired and footsore. They were hungry too. When no kind people gave them food, they helped themselves from the gardens and the shops and were driven away and beaten. Some of them fell ill and died.

At last, the band of boys and girls came to the seashore, but they found the waves rolling up the beach just as usual. No dry pathway through the water was to be seen. A

The children at the seashore

few of them waded into the sea, but they soon came back again.

Tired and hungry and sad, the poor children did not know what to do. Kind strangers took some of them into their houses to live with their own children. But most of them roamed to and fro on the shore, thinking sadly of Jerusalem and of their homes far away.

Then they were told of ships, which were to sail across the sea. The captains of these ships said they would take the children to the Holy Land without payment, "for the love of God." But they did not mean what they said.

The boys and girls crowded joyfully onto the ships. They were happy, for they thought that all was well and that they would now reach Jerusalem.

The ships sailed away, but they did not go to the Holy Land. The captains were cruel and wicked men. They took the children to another land and sold them as slaves.

So the poor little Soldiers of the Cross never saw Jerusalem. Nor did they ever go back to their homes.

But the story of their sorrows was told in many lands and to many people. When they heard it, a great many strong men set out for Jerusalem to fight the battles, which the children had hoped to fight.

I am glad to tell you that the wicked captains were caught and punished as they deserved.

10
King John and the Abbot

KING John was one of the kings of England. He was a wicked man, who did much more evil than good during his reign, for he was so selfish that he did not like to see anyone in his kingdom have anything, which he himself could not have. His people hated him, because he treated them harshly and took their property away from them to aid in his own pleasure.

Now in the town of Canterbury, there was a rich old abbot, who lived in a fine large house, called the abbey. He was very kind and gentle, so that all who knew him loved him. Everyone who passed his way was welcome to stop at his house. Indeed, his abbey became so famous that it was always full of people.

It often happened that as many as two or three hundred people would sit down to dinner with this good abbot. Not only the poor but also many brave knights, dressed in velvet and beautiful furs, came to visit here.

When King John heard of this, he was very angry. The abbot was living in finer fashion than the king himself. This made the king jealous, so he decided to put a stop to the abbot's fine dinners. He sent for the old man and had him brought before his throne.

"How now, good Abbot," said King John. "They tell me that you sit down to dinner with hundreds of guests and that in all ways you live in finer style than I. No man should live better than his king, and I shall see that no man does."

The old abbot answered with fear, "I pray thy mercy, O king. I did but use that which was mine in the way that seemed to me best. I have wealth and broad lands. I can think of no better way of using them than to give meat and drink to those who stop at my door and ask for aid. Surely I should not be blamed for doing what I can to make life pleasant for the brave knights and the poor peasants who are about me."

"How can I not blame you?" was the reply. "I, John, am England's king. All the lands and all the crops and all the gold in this whole country are mine by right. If you have more than you need, you shall turn your lands over to me. I will decide what shall be done with them."

"Oh, say not so!" cried the abbot, and he fell on his face before the king to beg for mercy.

At last, the king yielded. "One chance," said he, "will I give thee. But you must answer me two questions. If you fail to make good answer to either of the two, your head shall be cut off, and all your riches shall be mine."

"I will try my best, O king," replied the abbot, for he was glad to have even this little chance to escape the king's wrath.

"Well, then," began the king, "in the first place, you must tell me, as I sit here with my crown of gold upon my head, how long I shall live. See to it that you do not miss the answer by so much as a day. In the second place, you must tell me of what I am thinking while you are trying to answer my first question."

"O, king," said the abbot, "these questions are too hard indeed to be answered at once. Give me two weeks in which to think, and I will do my best to answer them."

"Two weeks you shall have," was the reply, "but remember, if you fail, you shall lose your head and your lands shall be mine."

The abbot went back to his abbey, sad and in great fear, but, no matter how hard he tried, he could think of no answer to the king's questions. He asked all the knights and ladies who came to the abbey, but not one could tell him what answers to make to the king.

He then rode to the town of Oxford, where a great school and many wise men were. But none of them could help him. So the abbot went on to Cambridge, where there was another school. He told his trouble to the wise men there, too. All of them liked the poor abbot and tried to think of some way to help him. But not one of them could answer the two questions.

Finally the poor abbot gave up hope. Sadly he turned back toward his great abbey. The end of the two weeks was near, and he wished to bid farewell to his friends before going to his death.

Just before the abbot reached his own gate, he met his shepherd going out to the fields for his sheep.

"Welcome, good master," cried the shepherd. "What good news do you bring us of your search?"

"Alas," answered the abbot, "there is no good news to bring. No man can tell me what I shall say to the king that I may save my head."

The shepherd stood up straight. "I bid you be of good cheer, master. I may be able to help you. Before now, a fool has taught a wise man wit."

"What," cried the abbot, "you help me? How can you be of any help to me in this trouble?"

"People have said many times," replied the shepherd, "that I look very much like you. Sometimes I have even been mistaken for you. If that is true, when we dress in such different clothes, surely no one could tell us apart if I wore your cloak and your cap. Lend me your horse, your cloak, your staff, and your servants, and I will go to London. If nothing else, at least, I can die in your place."

"My good shepherd," said the abbot, "you shall not die in my place. If the worst comes to the worst, I shall die for myself, but I have a mind to let you try your plan and see if good may come of it."

So it happened that the very next day the shepherd made ready to go to London. Over

The shepherd before King John

his plain shepherd's dress, he put the abbot's long cloak. On his head, he wore the abbot's fine cap, and, in his hand, he carried a golden staff. Dressed in his master's clothes, the shepherd looked so much like the abbot that no one could have told that he was not the great man himself. He then mounted the abbot's horse, and, together with a great following of servants, he started to London.

When this party arrived in the city, they went straightway to the palace, where the shepherd was shown before the king.

When King John saw the shepherd, he did not doubt that he was the abbot.

"I welcome you, Sir Abbot," he said. "It is well that you have come back to me. Can you give me the answers to my two questions? Remember, if you fail to answer either, you are to lose your head."

"O, king, I remember," said the shepherd. "But I think I can answer both your questions."

King John laughed at this, for he did not think any man could answer the questions.

"Well, since you think you can answer my questions, tell me, how long shall I live? Be sure that you tell me the truth."

The shepherd looked at the king and said, "O, king, you shall live until you die, and not one day longer; and you shall die when you take your last breath, and not one minute sooner."

This answer made the king laugh.

"You are a witty fellow, Sir Abbot," he said.

"Your answer to the first question is right, but you must also answer another. Now tell me of what I am thinking while you are standing before me."

The shepherd was ready to answer this question also. "That is, indeed, an easy question," he said. "You are thinking that the Abbot of Canterbury stands before you. But there you are wrong, O king, for I am only a poor shepherd, who has come to beg your pardon for both my master and myself." With these words, the shepherd threw off the abbot's long cloak.

When the king saw that he had been deceived by the shepherd, he laughed loudly and long.

"You are certainly a witty, merry fellow," said the king. "Indeed, you are so witty that I am going to make you the Abbot of Canterbury in place of your master."

"That cannot be," answered the shepherd, "for I can neither read nor write."

The king knew that what the shepherd said

was true. "You are right, my merry fellow," he said. "You could not be an abbot. But I will give you something to pay you for your wit. Every week, for the rest of your life, I will send you four pieces of silver. And now you may go. When you get home, tell your master that he is free and that it was your wit, which brought him the king's pardon."

11
William Tell

Six hundred years ago, the Swiss people were ruled by men from another country. These rulers treated the people very badly.

One of the rulers was a bad and cruel man.

He set up a pole in the market place of a Swiss town and hung his hat upon it. Then he said that all who passed by must bow to the hat.

This was a foolish thing. The people were proud and did not wish to bow to the ruler's hat, but they feared he would kill them if they did not do so. So some of them bowed, but it was with anger and hate in their hearts.

Yet there was one man who would not bow to the hat. He was a bold hunter, and his name was William Tell.

Tell will not bow to the hat.

He passed the pole three times, but he did not bow. When this was told to the ruler, he was very angry.

"That man shall die," said he.

But he did not kill Tell at once. He said he would save the hunter's life if he would, with his bow and arrow, shoot an apple from the head of his own little son.

It was a cruel thing to ask, for the sharp arrow might strike the boy's head instead of the apple. The ruler hoped that this would happen, and then he would kill Tell.

But no man could shoot better than the bold hunter. He set an apple upon his boy's head. The child was not afraid, for he trusted his father.

Then Tell drew his bow and shot the arrow. Its sharp point stuck into the apple and cut it into pieces, but it did not hurt the boy.

The people shouted with joy, but the ruler was angry. He saw another arrow in the hunter's belt.

"What is that arrow for?" asked he. "If I

This building stands on the rock where Tell is said to have jumped ashore.

had hurt my boy, I should have shot that arrow into your heart," said Tell.

These bold words made the ruler more angry than before.

"Take that man to prison," cried he. So Tell was thrown into a boat and rowed across the lake to a strong castle.

But, on the way, a storm arose, and, while they were trying to land, Tell jumped ashore. He hid himself in the high mountains, and, when the ruler came to find him, the hunter shot him dead with an arrow.

So the Swiss people were rid of a cruel man. To this day, they love to speak of the brave Tell.

12
How a Strong Castle was Taken

ONE evening when it was nearly dark, a woman sat upon the high wall of a castle in Scotland. She held her baby in her arms, and she sang to lull it to sleep.

This woman was the wife of an English soldier. The castle was full of English soldiers, for the King of England had taken it away from the Scots.

This is the song which the woman sang:

> "Hush ye, hush ye, little pet ye,
> Hush ye, hush ye, do not fret ye,
> The Black Douglas shall not get ye."

Douglas was a leader of the Scots. He was

a big man with black hair, and he was brave and clever. He had made up his mind to win the strong castle back for the Scots.

The woman did not know the Black Douglas was near when she sang that song to her baby. The soldiers also did not know, or they would have watched more carefully than they did.

By and by, the woman looked down and saw some black things moving on the ground outside the castle wall. She pointed to them.

"What are those things?" said she to a soldier.

The man looked down from the wall. "They are only bullocks," said he. "They must have strayed from the farm yonder." Then he walked away.

The woman went on singing to her baby:

"Hush ye, hush ye, do not fret ye,
The Black Douglas shall not get ye."

All at once a voice said: "Do not be so sure

of that." The woman started and looked round. There beside her was "Black Douglas" himself. He had climbed the wall.

Other Scots were close behind him. These men were the black things, which the woman had seen moving upon the ground. They wore black cloaks and crept upon their hands and knees. That is why in the dusk they looked like bullocks.

Douglas and his men opened the gates of the castle before the English soldiers could stop them. Then a strong band of Scots rushed in, and the castle was taken.

Many of the English were killed in that fight. But Douglas saved the life of the woman who had sat upon the wall singing to her baby.

13

A King Learns a Lesson

ONE of the greatest of the Scotch kings was Robert Bruce. He was very wise and very brave, and it was good for Scotland that the country had such a king. For at that time, the king of England, who wanted to take Scotland for himself, had led a great army into that country.

The war had lasted a long time, and Robert Bruce had almost lost heart. Six times had he led his army against the English; six times had his men been beaten and driven back. It now seemed that Scotland must give up, that it was impossible for the Scots to win. Bruce's army had been scattered, and even he, the king, had been forced to find a hiding-place for himself.

As he wandered through the wood alone, this unhappy king came upon a wretched old hut. He entered and lay down on some straw to rest, for he was very tired from his journey through the forests and among the mountains.

It was a dreary day. As Bruce lay there on the straw, he listened to the rain as it pattered down on the roof of his hiding-place. He was tired and lonely.

Robert Bruce watching the spider

It seemed to him that there was no longer any use for him to try to drive the English from Scotland. He felt that he could do nothing but give up to his foes.

But as he lay there, he happened to look up. Above him, hanging from the roof of the hut, he saw a spider making ready to spin her web. He watched the little thing as she worked. She was trying to swing to the next rafter and so build her thin web. Six times she tried, and six times she failed. Then she stopped. Bruce thought she had given up.

"Poor little spider, you are just like me," he said. "Six times have we both tried, and six times have we failed. We can do no more."

But just then the spider began to move again. Slowly and with care, she tried to swing herself across to the next rafter.

Bruce watched her closely. He wondered if she would fail again. But the spider did not fail; this time she reached the other rafter.

When the king saw that the little spider had

swung herself across in safety, he took heart and sprang up from his resting-place.

"You have taught me a lesson, my brave little friend," he said. "I, too, will try again."

Then Bruce went out and called some of his men to him. They were pleased when he told them that he was ready to meet his foes again. All were willing to help him. Messages were at once sent to all parts of Scotland asking the Scots to gather around their brave king.

The army, which came in answer to these messages, was not a large one, but the soldiers were brave. Although they knew that the king of England had three times as many men as Robert Bruce had, these brave Scots did not lose heart.

A hard fought battle followed, but, in the end, Bruce and his men forced the English back. England's king was then ready to leave the Scots alone. The Battle of Bannockburn, for that is the name of this great battle, was won by Bruce and his Scots. Scotland was free from her foes forever, and all because her king had learned a good lesson from a little spider.

14
Dick Whittington

You all know the story of Dick Whittington and his cat. Perhaps you think it is only a fairy tale and that Dick was not a real person at all. If you think so, you make a mistake.

Dick Whittington was alive in England about five hundred years ago. He was Lord Mayor of London three times, just as the story says.

Dick's father and mother died when he was a young boy. Then he was very unhappy at home. So he went to London and worked in the house of a rich merchant.

This merchant had ships, which he sent across the sea. He filled his ships with fine and useful things to be sold to the people of other lands.

This is what the story tells us. One day the merchant asked his servants if they would like to put something into his ship. So each servant sent something to be sold in lands across the sea.

Dick sent a cat. He was poor and had nothing else to send. His cat was sold for some pieces of gold in a land where there were many mice and rats, but no cats to catch them.

This gold was a help to Dick. He worked hard and soon made more money, and, by and by, he became a rich merchant like his old master.

Then he was made Lord Mayor of London, once, twice, three times. The last time he was mayor, he gave a fine feast for the king and queen. And the king made him a knight and called him Sir Richard Whittington.

Sir Richard did not spend all his money on himself. He was very kind to the poor and gave them food and clothes.

He gave money to build churches, too, and

helped to build a hospital for poor, sick people.

In those days, the prisons were dreadful places. They were dark and small, and there was no good fresh air in them. Many men and women fell sick and died in prison.

A monument to Sir Richard Whittington

Sir Richard was very sorry for the poor prisoners. So he gave money to make one of the prisons in London a larger and better place.

15
Joan of Arc

LONG ago a young girl named Joan lived in a farmhouse in France. Joan played with her brothers and sisters in a large forest near her home. She liked to listen to the wind among the trees, and she loved the little wild birds and beasts.

The birds and beasts loved Joan, too. They would come to her when she called them.

Joan was a good girl. She helped her mother to keep the house tidy and to spin and sew. Sometimes she went into the fields to mind the sheep.

Those were sad days for France, for there was fighting in the land. The English soldiers were there, and they had beaten the French soldiers in many battles.

The French prince was not a brave nor a wise man. He was afraid of his foes and did little to help his own people.

Some of the poor, wounded soldiers of France came to the village where Joan lived. Then the young girl gave up her bed to the sick men and helped her mother to nurse them. Her heart was full of pity for the fair land of France.

One day Joan heard a voice that told her to go and help her country. She thought it was an angel's voice. But at first she did not go. "How can a young girl like me help France?" she said.

Then the voice spoke to her again and again, and each time it told her to go and help the French prince.

At last, Joan made up her mind to go, for she was sure that God had sent an angel to speak to her.

The young girl's friends laughed.

"How can you help the prince?" they cried.

"You will do better to stay at home and mind the sheep."

"I would gladly stay by my mother's side," said Joan, "but I must go, for God wills it."

Her father at first tried to stop her, but in the end he let her go. She asked many people to help her, and at last a great man sent her to the prince.

The prince was not pleased to see her. "What can you do to help me?" he asked. "Can you ride to battle?"

"I can if God wills it," said Joan. "He wills that I shall help you to win the crown of France."

She said this again and again, till at last the prince thought she might be right. So he gave her a white suit of armor and a white banner and set her on a white horse.

Then he told her to lead his soldiers to battle.

The French soldiers thought their girl leader was an angel come down from heaven to help them. This thought made them brave when they marched to battle.

The English soldiers were afraid of her. So they did not fight well, and the French were able to beat them many times.

Very soon the French prince was crowned King of France, and Joan felt that her work was ended. She knelt before the king and said:

"Gentle king, God's will is done. Let me now go home to my brothers and sisters; they will be so glad to see me."

But the king did not want to let her go, for he feared that his soldiers would not be so brave without her. So poor Joan had to stay and go on fighting.

But she was sad. She longed to see her dear ones at home and to walk in the forest, which she loved so well.

The French soldiers lost heart when they saw how sad she was, and then they did not fight well. At last they were beaten, and poor Joan was put into prison by her foes.

The French king did not try to help her. So

she lay in prison for a long time.

Then the English took her out. They told her to say aloud before the people that she had done wrong and that she had not spoken truly when she said that angels had talked with her.

But Joan would not say those things.

The place where Joan of Arc was burned at Rouen

"I am a simple, country girl, and God only has helped me in all I have done," said she.

The English did not believe her. They said that she was a wicked girl and that she did not speak the truth. So they did a very cruel thing. They burned poor Joan to death.

That was nearly five hundred years ago. Today the English people are ashamed to think of this wicked deed.

The French people are ashamed, too, when they remember their weak king, who did nothing to help the brave young girl who had done so much for him and for the fair land of France.

16
The Story of Printing

ONE day, about five hundred years ago, an old man named Coster went for a walk in the woods near his home in Holland. When he was tired, he sat down to rest upon a log.

There was bark upon the log. Coster peeled some bark from the log and cut it into letters A, and B, and C with his knife. The letters were for his little grandchildren at home.

He rolled the letters he had made in a piece of parchment and tied them up into a parcel. Parchment is a sort of paper made from skin.

When the old man reached home, he opened the parcel and took out the letters. He looked at the paper in surprise. There were marks A, and B, and C upon it. The bark, of which the letters were made, had been damp, and it had marked the paper with the shape of the letters.

The letters were not very clear, but they could be read. When Coster saw them, he began to think.

"Why should not books be printed from letters wet with ink?" said he to himself.

In those days there were very few books, and they were very costly. They were not

Lettering a book by hand

printed as our books are, because men did not then know how to print. All books were written, and every letter was made by hand with pen and ink.

It took a long time to copy a book in this way. Sometimes a man would work at one book every day for two or three years. No wonder it cost much money when it was done.

Only rich people could buy books then. Most of the poor people did not even know how to read, for of what use was it to learn, if they had no books.

Coster tried to find out how to print books instead of writing them. He made many letters, first of wood and afterwards of metal. He smeared these letters with ink and pressed sheets of paper on them. He did this by hand. The inky letters made black marks on the paper, and the marks were shaped like the letters.

The old man was much pleased, for now he felt sure that books could be printed in this way.

Coster showed his printed letters to a clever young man from Germany.

This young man saw that Coster had found out something good and useful. But his way of printing took a long time.

So the young German set to work to find a quicker way. He worked hard, and, by and by, he made a machine for printing books. It was called a printing press.

The printing press had cases for holding the

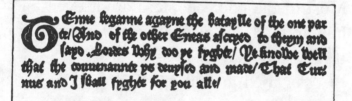

Part of a book printed by Caxton

letters. It had brushes for smearing the ink upon the letters, and it had a press for pressing the sheets of paper down upon the inky letters.

With a printing press, a hundred copies of a book could be printed in a few days. What a wonderful thing these clever men had found out!

About that time, an Englishman named Caxton lived in a land across the sea. He

An early printing press

copied books in writing for a great lady.

Caxton grew very tired of this work. He said his hand was tired from holding a pen and his eyes were dim from looking at white paper.

He was very glad to hear of this new machine for printing books. He learned how to print, and then he made a printing press for himself and took it to England.

Caxton set up a small shop in London, and

there he put his press. He printed books of all sorts. There were story books, prayer books, poetry books, and books of travel.

Crowds of people came to his shop to see the wonderful machine, which could print a book in one day. Some of the people took written books with them and asked Caxton to print them.

Sometimes the king went to the printer's shop to talk with him and hear about his work.

A picture from an old book

Caxton's press was never idle. The books he printed were much cheaper than written books. Now it was not only rich men who could buy them. People who had a little money were also able to buy a book to read.

Men and women, who did not know how to read, now began to learn and to teach their children. And people grew wiser and better because they had good books to read.

17

The Finding of the New World

THERE was once a boy in the sunny land of Italy whose name was Columbus.

This boy lived at the seaside. He loved the sea. He liked to talk to the sailors and hear their tales of far away lands. And he liked to read books about travel.

Sometimes he sailed in a ship to strange places. But he did not go far from home. Men did not go far across the sea in those days, for they did not think it was safe to do so. They did not know that there were lands on the other side of the sea.

But young Columbus thought that the world was a very big place.

"I am sure I should find new and wonderful

lands, if I could sail far across the sea," said he.

At first, he could not do so. He was poor and had no money to buy ships or to pay sailors to go with him.

When he was a man, he asked kings and queens and rich men to help him. But, for a long time, nobody would give him money.

At last, when he had been to many places and asked many people, he got help. The Queen of Spain got him three ships and a hundred men. She said she would make him a rich man, if he should find new lands.

Then Columbus was very happy. He made his ships ready and sailed away with his men over the wide, blue sea.

At first, all went well. So long as the ships were near land, the sailors were content. But when they had sailed a long way and no land was to be seen, the men felt afraid.

"These little ships are not safe in this big sea," said they. "We must go back." And they looked angrily at their leader because he had taken them such a long way from home.

Columbus spoke gaily to them.

"Wait a little longer," said he. "We shall soon reach another land beyond the sea."

So the three little ships sailed on and on, over the wide blue sea. The days passed, and the weeks passed, and still no new land was found.

Then the sailors lost heart. "We will go no farther," they cried. "We will turn the ships round and go back to Spain."

Their brave leader was sad. "Wait only three days longer," said he. "If we do not then see land, I will myself turn the ships and go back."

So the sailors said they would wait for three days longer.

Soon after this, some bits of wood were seen floating upon the water. The wood had strange marks upon it, as if someone had been cutting it.

"That wood has come from the land," said Columbus. "We shall soon be there."

By and by, some birds flew past. "Those are

land birds," said Columbus. And he steered his ships so as to follow them.

Then a branch of a tree was found in the sea. There were red berries upon the branch, and these berries were quite fresh. So all the men knew that land must be near.

Landing in the New World

Next day a green island was seen. It was part of the New World beyond the sea. Then there was joy among the men. They threw themselves down at the feet of Columbus and begged him to forgive them. They knew now what a wise and brave leader he was.

Columbus and his men landed on the island, and the people who lived there crowded round them. Instead of wearing clothes, they put paint upon their skins. They were full of wonder to see the white men and their clothes, and boots, and their strange ships.

But the white men did not stay long. They sailed away and found some other islands. Then they went back to Spain. What a wonderful story they had to tell of new lands, and strange people, and animals, and birds, and flowers!

When the other seamen heard that Columbus had come back safe, they were no longer afraid to sail far away from home. Many of them went across the sea in their ships to see for themselves the new lands that had been found.

Some went farther still and found other lands in the New World. The great land, which is now called America, was one of these.

18
The Great Fire of London

WHEN a house is set on fire in these days, firemen rush with their engines to put it out. But, in old days, there were no firemen and no fire engines. A fire was then a much more dreadful thing than it is now.

Once upon a time, nearly all the big city of London was burned to ashes. The fire began on a windy night, at a baker's shop in a narrow street.

The strong wind blew the flames from the baker's house to the next, and then to the next. Very soon all the houses in the street were blazing. They were made of wood, so they burned very quickly.

Before long, the fire spread to other narrow

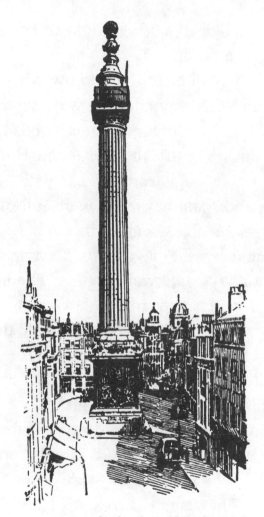

This stone tower marks the place where the fire began.

streets of wooden houses. What a dreadful
sight it was! Sparks flew about, flames

blazed and crackled, and roofs and chimneys fell with a crash.

The poor people did not know what to do. They ran this way and that way, screaming. Many of them dragged their goods out of their houses to try to save them. But there were not enough carts to carry the things away, and soon the streets were full of beds, and broken tables, and chairs.

By and by, the pavements became so hot that nobody could walk on them. People ran to the river and rowed away in boats. Thousands went to the fields outside the city.

The fire kept on burning for three days. Hundreds of houses and many churches and schools were burned to the ground.

Then someone found a way to stop it. A great many houses were blown up with gunpowder. This made wide gaps in the streets. The flames died out slowly when they reached these gaps, for they could not leap over them to the houses on the other side.

The people of London were very brave. They soon set to work to build up their city and to build their houses.

So the new London was a better place to live in than the old one. A tall tower of stone was built to mark the place where the great fire began, and there you may see it still.

19

A Wild Boy — Robert Clive

ONE day there was a crowd in the market-place of a little English town. People looked up and pointed. There at the top of the church tower, a boy was sitting. He had climbed the high tower. The people got ladders and brought him down safely.

That boy was young Robert Clive. He was a wild, careless boy, who loved to run and to play soldier. This made his father sad, for he feared his boy would not be a good and useful man.

But he made a mistake. Robert was wild and idle, but he was not a bad boy. When his school days were over, he went to India to work for some merchants.

Clive Street, Calcutta, India
Clive once lived in a house on this street.

He had to sit on a stool and write letters, and add up figures. He did not do this work well, for he hated to sit still. The merchants were not pleased with him.

But, by and by, a change came. There was a fight in India between the English merchants and the French merchants.

Young Clive was sent out to fight for the English merchants. He did this well, for he liked it. By and by, he was made a prisoner.

But the boy who could climb a church tower was able to find a way out of prison. He got away safely and went back to the merchants.

The fighting was not yet over, and Clive wanted to go back there. "Let me go," said he. "I can fight better than I can write."

So the merchants let him go.

Clive watching the work of his guns

The young man was right. He could fight well, and he was a brave soldier. Before long, he was made a captain and led his men to battle against a great ruler of India. The battle was won, and a part of India was taken.

That was the first part of India to be ruled by the British.

20
The Boy Nelson

NELSON was one of the bravest sailors who ever lived, and one of the best loved. In another book you will read of some of the things, which he did when he was a man.

But he was brave long before he was grown up; he was a brave boy.

It is not only big, strong boys and girls who are brave. Nelson was not a big, strong child; he was small and weak, and he was often ill. But he was never afraid.

When he was a very little boy, he went to stay with his grandmother. One day, he set out alone to look for birds' nests. He did not come home to dinner.

The hours passed by, but still he did not

come back. His grandmother feared that he was lost, so she sent a servant to look for him.

The servant found him far away. He was sitting on the bank of a stream, which was too wide and deep for him to cross.

"I wonder, child, that hunger and fear did

not drive you home," said his grandmother.

"Fear, Grandmamma!" said little Nelson. "What is fear? I never saw it."

Nelson was only about twelve years old when he sailed on a ship to the cold sea near the North Pole. The ship was frozen in the ice, and, for some weeks, it could not move.

One night, young Nelson and another boy crept away from the ship and walked across the ice. They wanted to hunt a bear.

It was dark and foggy. Nobody saw the boys go, but very soon the sailors missed them and went to look for them. When daylight came, the two boys were seen far away from the ship. They had found a big bear and were trying to kill it.

"Come back!" shouted the sailors, who feared that the bear would kill the boys. But young Nelson would not come back. So the sailors fired a gun, and, at the sound of the gun, the big bear ran away.

When the boys came back to the ship, they were well scolded for being so rash.

"Why did you do such a thing?" asked the captain.

"I wanted a bearskin for my father," said young Nelson.

He was not afraid when he was a boy, and he was not afraid when he grew to be a man. That is why he did so many brave things.

He became a great sea captain and led the British ships to battle.

21
The Boy Napoleon

WHEN you read big books of history, you will find many stories about Napoleon. He was not a large man, but he was one of the best soldiers the world has seen.

Napoleon loved to fight, and he began to fight when he was a boy. He was a Corsican boy, and he went to school in France.

He was not bright at his lessons. He liked to dig in the garden of the school and to walk alone. Most of all, he liked to play at battles or to read about them in books.

One winter it was very cold. The snow was deep on the ground. The playground with its coat of snow seemed just the place for a game.

"Let us go out!" said young Napoleon to the other boys. "I will show you a fine game to play in the snow."

The boys ran out into the playground. Then Napoleon showed them how to dig passages in the snow and how to make it into walls, and forts, and trenches. He had read about these things in his books about battles.

When the teachers saw how busy and happy the boys were, they did not stop their game.

By and by, all was ready. Then the boys had a battle. There were two parties of boys, and Napoleon was the leader of one party. He and his young soldiers hid behind the snow walls and forts on one side of the playground, while the rest of the boys went to the other side. They fought with snowballs.

The snow lasted for a long time. For many days, the boys ran out, when lessons were done, to play at battles.

But, at last, some of the young soldiers were hurt with stones, which were put into the snowballs. Then the teachers stopped the game.

Many of these boys, who played at soldiers in the snow, became real soldiers when they were men. But Napoleon was the best soldier of them all.

He was the leader of the French soldiers. His men loved and trusted him. They were always brave when he was with them, so they won many battles.

But they were beaten at last by the British in a big fight. Some day, you will read about this fight and about the brave British leader who beat the great Napoleon.

Napoleon

22

The Little Corporal

WHEN Napoleon was a young man, his country was at war with Austria. It was a terrible war, and brave men were needed to lead the French soldiers against their foe. Among the men chosen for this work was the young Napoleon.

Now, Napoleon was not only young, but he was very small and very thin as well. At first glance, everyone took him to be just a poor, weak, little man who had better be keeping shop than fighting. But there was something in his face that made people turn to look a second time. Then they saw that they had been mistaken. His eyes were sharp and bright; he seemed to see everything at once.

Napoleon leading his men across the bridge

When Napoleon reached his soldiers, he found them ragged and hungry, cold, and hopeless. At the first sight of their new officer, they wanted to make fun of him. Surely such a man could not lead an army, they thought. But they soon changed their minds, for Napoleon began to talk to them.

"Soldiers," he said, "you are hungry. You haven't enough clothing to keep you warm. France owes you a great deal but can do nothing for you. But I will lead you into a rich country. There you shall win great cities. You shall find not only riches, but you shall find glory as well. Soldiers of France, will you follow me?"

As they listened to Napoleon's cheering words, the soldiers forgot their hunger and cold. They began to like their new leader at once, and they no longer wanted to laugh at him. In this way, he won the love of his men.

Later they found that this man, small though he was, was not afraid of danger. He shared their troubles and risked his life as though he were a common soldier. Soon there was not a man among them who did not love and worship him.

Many times Napoleon led his soldiers against the Austrians. Before a year had passed, he had fought more than a dozen battles, and each time he had won.

One of the greatest of these battles was the one fought at the little town of Lodi. The French had pursued the Austrians to that place, but they could go no farther, for before them lay the river Adda.

To cross this river, they had to pass over a small bridge, called the Bridge of Lodi.

The Austrians had already crossed the river. Of course, they wanted to keep the French from following, so they placed their guns near the bridge. If Napoleon and his men should try to pass, they would shoot them down.

But Napoleon did not let this stop him. He ordered some of his best soldiers to rush ahead and take the bridge.

"But it is impossible," said one of these men.

"Impossible?" asked Napoleon. "In our language there is no such word as 'impossible.'"

Encouraged by these words, the men rushed on. But scarcely had they touched the bridge when they were shot down by the Austrians. Still others tried to take the bridge, but all were struck by Austrian bullets, and all fell wounded.

Those who were left stopped short. They did not want to be killed. For a moment it seemed that the French were going to lose the battle.

But, just then, Napoleon himself snatched the banner from the hands of the corporal, or color-bearer. Waving the flag above his head, he called to his men to follow him. The soldiers dashed after their beloved leader. In a few minutes, the French were holding the bridge, and the Austrians were fleeing on all sides.

After this victory at the Bridge of Lodi, the French soldiers always called their leader "The Little Corporal." It was a name Napoleon loved very dearly.

23
Australia

On the other side of our round world, there is a very big island called Australia.

There are fine cities in Australia now and large farms where thousands of sheep feed. And there are orchards full of fruit trees and wide plains where gold is found.

In the old days, this was not so. When George III was King of England, people knew very little about this big land.

So, by his order, a ship was made ready. A brave sailor named Cook was made captain of the ship and sent to the other side of the world to look for new lands.

Captain Cook sailed away far over the sea and found a great many islands. On one of

Captain Cook

these, they found old stone idols, some of which had fallen down.

At last, they came to an island far bigger than any of the others and nearly as large as Europe. This was the land that is now called Australia.

He landed on the shore with his men and put up the British flag. This was to show all men that he had taken the land for the king.

There were no towns, no railways, and no roads in Australia then. It was a wild land, and no white men lived there. A few aborigines roamed in the woods, killed the wild animals and birds, and fished in the rivers.

Captain Cook sailed back to England and told the king about the new country that he had found. Soon after that, other ships sailed

Captain Cook on board his ship

over the sea to Australia. They were full of British men, women, and children.

These people took with them their beds, and chairs, and tables. They took seeds, too, and wagons and tools, and horses, and cattle, and sheep, for they meant to build houses, make farms, and grow grain in the new land.

At first, these people from Britain did not find Australia a good land to live in.

They packed their children and their goods

into their wagons and drove their cattle and sheep before them. Then they marched out into the wild country.

But they did not go far. Soon they came to some high mountains. There they stopped, for their horses could not go up the rocky sides of the mountains.

They cut down trees, built houses of wood to live in, and planted their seeds. But the seeds did not come up. And this is why.

It is autumn in Australia when it is springtime in the northern hemisphere, and the summer sun shines in Australia when ice and snow are in the North.

A farm in Australia

The newcomers did not know these things. They planted their seeds at the wrong time, and that is why they did not come up.

The poor people had other troubles too. Many of their sheep ate bad weeds and died. Some of their cattle were lost in the woods. Often they had not enough to eat, or the streams dried up so there was no water to drink. Sometimes the aborigines burned their houses and stole their sheep and cattle.

It was a sad time. Many of the settlers died; some lost heart and said: "Let us go home again; this is not a good land for us."

But many others were brave. They made up their minds they would not be beaten. These were the men who made Australia a great land.

They soon found out the right time to plant their seeds and began to grow grains and fruits. By and by, they made a way across the high mountains. On the other side of the mountains, they found good grass for their sheep. Some of them found gold.

A Kangaroo
The kangaroo is a common animal in Australia.

Before long, other people from Britain
sailed across the sea to help their brave
friends. After a time, towns were built, and

good roads and railways were made.

Today, Australia is one of the best lands of all. And the people are busy, and rich, and happy.

They send many good things to the markets of Britain. Wool, and wood, and fruit, and butter, and meat are some of these things.

Index with Pronuciation Guide
Proununciation Key

This list of the most important names in the book tells you on what page you may find each name and how to sound those you may not know.

Sound	In These Words	Sound	In These Words
a	map, pat	o	pot, stop
ā	ate, face	ō	over, go
â	care, pair	ô	order, all
ä	far, farther		
		u	cut, butter
e	pet, west, head		
ē	wc, meet	oi	boil, voice
		ou	shout, house
i	in, bit		
ī	nice, tiger	o͝o	pull, put
		o͞o	rule, move, use, music

ə represents:

a	in about	o	in lemon
e	in token	i	in happily
	u	in circus	

Tales from Far and Near

Index

D

E

F

G

H

I

Index

Tales of Long Ago

Edited by
Arthur Guy Terry
Associate Professor of History
Northwestern University

History Stories of Other Lands

List of Stories

1

How Men and Women
Were Found for Rome

YOU will remember the story of Romulus, the man who built the city of Rome upon the hills near a river in Italy.

Now, a city needs people, and, when Rome was first built, there were very few people in it. Romulus knew that his city would not grow big and strong unless there were plenty of men to work for it and to fight for it. He knew, too, that there must be women to spin and sew, to take care of the children, to cook, and to keep the houses tidy.

This story tells how he found men and women for Rome.

To begin with, he said that any person, who liked to do so, might come to Rome and make his home there. As soon as this was known, men came to the city from many places. Some of these men were good and honest. But others were bad men who had been turned out of their own cities because of the wrong things they had done.

Romulus let them all come into Rome, as he had promised to do. Perhaps he hoped the bad men would do better in their new home. A few of the men brought their wives and daughters with them, but most of them came alone. Romulus now had to find wives for these men.

At first, he asked the people of other cities to let their daughters marry the Romans. But the people of the other cities would not hear of such a thing.

"Your Romans are not good men," they said. "We will not let our daughters marry them."

When the men of Rome heard this saying, they made up their minds to get wives in another way. It was a very rough and rude way, but in those old days people did many

Roman boys running a foot race

rough and rude things.

The plan was to have a feast in Rome on a certain day and to have games and sports. Romulus asked the men of two other cities to come to see the games and sports and to bring their wives and children with them.

Many of these men came as they were asked to do. And with them came their wives and the young men and maidens, their sons and daughters. It was a merry time, and all were gay and happy.

The visitors did not think of danger, as they walked to and fro in the fields of Rome or stood in a crowd to look at the games and sports. But danger was near.

All at once there was a great noise and stir. Men ran to and fro and shouted; women screamed; the games were stopped. What was the matter?

The young men of Rome had rushed into

The Peacemakers

the crowd of visitors and laid hold of the young maidens of the other cities. Each Roman had taken a maiden for himself and was carrying her away to his house in the city to be his wife.

What a din there was! Fathers tried to save their daughters, and brothers tried to save their sisters. But it was of no use. The Romans drew their swords and would not give up the maidens. That was the rough way in which women were found for the new city of Rome.

The rest of the visitors went home to their own cities, sad and angry. But the men soon came back to Rome with a large army of soldiers. They meant to fight until they had won their daughters and sisters back again.

The Romans shut themselves up in the strong places on the hills of their city. For some time, the Romans kept their foes outside of the walls, but one day they were beaten in a fight, and the men of the other cities got into one of these strong places.

The husbands gave gifts to their wives.

After that, there were some fierce battles. The men of Rome fought fiercely for their wives, and the men of the other cities fought fiercely for their daughters and sisters. Sometimes one side won a battle, and sometimes the other won. A great many men were killed, but the fighting still went on, for neither side would give in.

The Roman wives were very sad. They loved their fathers and brothers, but they now loved their husbands too, for they were very kind to them. These poor women could not bear to see their husbands and their fathers and brothers killing each other. So they tried to make peace between them.

They rushed down into the battlefield and threw themselves between the fierce men and begged them to stop fighting for their sakes.

And because they loved their wives and their daughters, the husbands and fathers listened to the words of the women. They stopped the battle and became friends one with the other.

In this way, peace was made by the women.

After that time, a feast was held in Rome on one day in every year. It was called the Feast of the Women. On that day, the Roman husbands gave presents to their wives because of this good thing, which they had done.

2

How A Farmer Saved Rome

In the old days of Rome, there lived a worthy man who was called Cincinnatus. Cincinnatus was not this man's real name, but only a nickname given to him because of his long, curly hair. He was a very wise and brave man. He was not only wise and brave, but he was very different from most men of his time. He cared nothing for wealth and power, and, indeed, he liked nothing so well as to live simply on his small farm outside the walls of Rome.

There, on his farm, Cincinnatus spent his days, plowing his land, planting his seeds, and looking after his crops. He did not envy the men in Rome who were ruling the city and gaining great riches.

He was happy to live the simple life of a farmer.

The people in Rome knew of the wisdom of this farmer. They often went to him to get him to help them out of their troubles. Whenever anyone was in need of advice, he would say, "Well, I shall go see Cincinnatus. He will be able to help me."

Now it happened that at this time Rome was at war with a tribe of fierce people who lived near-by. These savage men were very cruel to their neighbors, the Romans. They burned the small towns and robbed the people who lived outside the walls of Rome. They even boasted that they would march to the very walls of Rome itself, enter the city, burn the houses, and kill the people.

When the chief men of Rome heard of this threat, they began to gather an army together. Every man who was able to fight became a soldier. Only the white-haired old men who ruled the city, a few guards, and the young boys stayed behind to look after the women

Mountain men attacking the Romans

and children. The army that went out from Rome was the largest and bravest in the world at that time. Everybody thought it would be an easy thing for such an army to drive their unfriendly neighbors back and to bring peace again to Rome.

But driving back the fierce men of the mountains was not so easy as it had at first seemed. As the Romans went to meet their enemy, they marched through a narrow valley between two mountains. These mountains were so high that no one could climb them. In front of the army was another mountain. It, also, was too steep to climb. The brave Roman leaders looked about and saw that they had been caught in a trap. There was only one way out. They must turn around and march out of the valley. There was no grass for their horses nor food for their men there. They must get out of the valley while they could.

But as the leaders turned to give the order to leave the valley, thousands of the savage mountain men sprang out from among the rocky cliffs. The army was entrapped in the valley. The Roman soldiers tried to draw their swords, but the pass was so narrow they could not fight. The mountain men then began to throw stones down upon the Romans, and it seemed that the brave Romans could do nothing to save themselves.

Just when everything seemed to be lost, five of the Roman soldiers who were riding in the back lines managed to escape from the valley. They spurred their horses and rode as hard as they could till they came to the walls of Rome.

They did not even stop at the city gates but rode straight to the market place. There they told the white-haired old men who ruled the city what had happened to the Roman soldiers.

When the City Fathers, for so they were called, heard this news, they were very much frightened.

"Oh, what shall we do ?" they cried. "We have no one whom we can send to help our army. The boys who were left at home are too young to go without a leader, and there is no man left who is wise enough to lead them. How can we save Rome?"

Everybody was very sad and very much afraid. It seemed that they could do nothing to save their army and that they would have to give up their city to their enemies, the savage mountain men.

But, at last, one of the City Fathers said,

"There is only one man who can save us. Let us send for Cincinnatus. He is wise, and he can help us out of our trouble."

Everybody thought this a very good plan, so the next morning some men went out to ask Cincinnatus to help them save their city. Early as it was, the good farmer was already at work in his fields. He was digging in the ground with his spade. Little did he dream that he, a simple farmer, had been chosen to save a great city.

"We bring you word from Rome," said the messengers, when they had found Cincinnatus.

"Is Rome in trouble ?" asked Cincinnatus.

The men then told him of Rome's danger and asked him to go with them and help to save the city. They also told him that the people of Rome had chosen him as ruler of their city and that everyone was ready to obey him. They told him he might do what he pleased with the city.

Cincinnatus called to his wife to bring his

cloak. When he had put it on, he told her of his call to the great city. Then, without another word, Cincinnatus hurried with the messengers to Rome, where he was greatly honored. The people cheered him as he passed through the streets, for they knew that he alone could save them. In order to do their part, they gladly did whatever Cincinnatus asked them to do.

First of all, wise Cincinnatus armed the boys and men who had been left to guard the city. Then he led them out to fight the enemy.

Within a few days, news reached Rome that Cincinnatus and his young soldiers had met the savage men of the mountains and had driven them back into their own country.

A few days later, Cincinnatus led the whole army back to Rome. The people were filled with joy to see their soldiers again and to know that their city was once more safe. They were so pleased with what Cincinnatus had done that they offered him a golden crown and wanted to make him king of Rome.

But Cincinnatus did not want to be a king. He thanked the people for the honor, which they had shown him. Then he went back to his little farm and spent the rest of his life as a simple farmer.

3

The Story of Marcius

SOMETIMES good and brave people, when they are very angry, do what is not right. There was once a great man of Rome who did a wrong thing when his heart was full of anger. His name was Marcius, and he was a very brave soldier.

Marcius loved Rome and wished to make it a strong and great city. He led the Roman soldiers against their foes and won many battles.

The people of Rome loved Marcius for his brave deeds. They gave him a new long name of honor, which you will learn some day.

But though Marcius was brave, he was not always wise and kind. Sometimes he did not treat the poor people fairly.

Poor Romans asking Marcius for better treatment

Poor people like to be free quite as much as rich people. Marcius treated them as if they were slaves. So they soon began to hate him. They said they would not bear to be treated in this way. But Marcius did not care what they said; he went on doing as he pleased.

Then the poor people hated him more and more. After a time, they forgot how much they owed him for his brave deeds and turned him out of the city. His rich friends were afraid to try to help him. So Marcius left Rome forever.

He was mad with anger. He was so angry that he forgot his love for Rome and forgot that he wished to see it rich and great. He thought only of the wrong that the people had done to him. He made up his mind to punish them by taking their city away from them and giving it to their foes.

This was not a good thing to do. It is not right for a man to try to hurt his own people and his own land. Marcius would not have done this thing if his heart had not been full of anger.

The angry Marcius went away to the foes of Rome and asked to see their leader. The leader's name was Tullus. He came out to speak to his visitor.

Then Marcius told Tullus that he had come to help him to take Rome away from the Romans.

Tullus knew well how strong and brave Marcius was, so he was glad to have his help. Soon a great army of soldiers was made ready, and Marcius led them to Rome.

The people of Rome were sorry for what they had done, when they heard that their old leader was coming to the city with a great army. They were afraid to fight against the brave and strong Marcius. So they sent ten of their chicf men to meet him and to beg him to forgive them.

Some of these men were old friends of Marcius. They begged him to remember their love for him and to spare the city for their sake.

But Marcius was too angry to listen to his friends. He spoke hard words to them and sent them back to Rome. Then a band of wise men came out of the city to beg for mercy. But they too were sent back with hard words.

The people of Rome were now in great fear. They thought that all was lost.

But the mother of Marcius made up her mind to try to save her city and her people. She could not bear to let her own son do a wrong and cruel deed. She took with her the wife of Marcius and his two little children, and some of the other great ladies of Rome, and went to the camp of the foes.

When Marcius came out to see them, these brave women and the little children knelt down upon the ground before him and begged him to forgive the people of Rome and spare the city.

Marcius loved his mother and his wife and children. His heart was full of sadness to see them kneel before him, and he could not be angry with them.

Tears came into his eyes, and he lifted them up and kissed them.

"Ah, Mother!" said he sadly. "You have saved Rome, but you have lost your son."

Marcius was right. He led the army of foes back to their own city, and Rome was saved. But Tullus was so angry with him for this deed that he killed him.

That was the end of the brave Marcius. He was a great man. But he would have been much greater if he had been kind as well as brave.

4

The Slave and the Lion

WE do not now think it right for anyone to be a slave. But, in old days, people saw no wrong in making men and women, and even little children, work for them as slaves.

The rich Romans kept many slaves to work in their houses and gardens and fields. Some of the Roman masters and mistresses were kind to their slaves and made them happy. Others were cruel and treated their slaves very cruelly. They beat them if they did not do well. Sometimes they even killed them.

There was once a slave in Rome who had a very cruel master. This slave's name was Androclus. He was so unhappy that at last he ran away. He hid himself in a cave in a wild

The lion held up its paw.

place, for he knew that his master would kill him if he found him.

By and by, a lion came into the cave. It was limping and seemed to be in great pain, and it roared loudly when it saw the slave.

The poor man was much afraid. He thought the lion would surely kill him and eat him. But the fierce beast did not even attack him. It stood still and held up its paw.

Then the slave saw that a sharp piece of wood was sticking in the lion's paw, which was swollen and sore. He was a kind man.

He took the animal's paw in his hand and gently pulled out the piece of wood.

This must have hurt the lion very much. But it lay quite still; it did not even growl. When the wood was out of its paw, it seemed very much pleased. It rubbed its head against the slave and made a soft, purring noise as if it were trying to thank him.

Soon after this, the slave was caught and taken back to his master. And, about the same time, some hunters caught the lion and sent it to the circus in Rome. Many wild beasts were kept there, and people used to go to look at them in their cages. Sometimes these beasts were let loose, and prisoners were thrown to them.

In those cruel times, the people of Rome liked to see fights between the prisoners and the lions and tigers. The wild beasts soon killed the poor men and women.

The cruel master of Androclus was so angry with him for running away that he said he should be thrown to the lions. So a day was fixed, and the poor slave was taken to the circus.

Crowds of people were there to watch the fight between a man and a lion. Men and women, and children too, went to see this dreadful sight.

They shouted and clapped their hands when the slave came into the circus ring. When the door of one of the cages was opened and a hungry lion sprang into the ring, they shouted and clapped again. They expected to see the fierce beast kill the man very quickly.

The lion gave a loud roar and began to creep towards the poor slave. The man gave himself up for lost. But, all at once, the animal's angry roar changed to a soft cry of pleasure. Instead of springing upon the slave, it ran to him and rubbed against him.

It was the lion from whose paw he had taken the sharp piece of wood, and it had not forgotten him. How glad the poor man was! He patted and stroked the faithful animal and spoke gently to it.

But the people were much surprised to see a man pat a fierce lion, as if it were a dog.

"What does this mean?" cried they. "Is the lion

tame? Has the man a charm for wild beasts?"

Then Androclus told his story. When the people heard how he had hidden in the lion's cave and pulled a piece of sharp wood from the fierce beast's paw, they were more surprised than ever.

"He is a brave man," they shouted. "We will not see him killed. Set him free. He shall no longer be a slave."

So Androclus was made a free man. He never went back to his cruel master. The story does not tell us whether the lion was set free, too, and allowed to go back to its cave. But we may hope it was.

Ruins of a great Roman Circus

5

A Clever Dog

In olden times, the Northmen were great sea-rovers. They sailed from Denmark and Norway across the sea in their fast boats, and fought with the people of other lands, and sometimes robbed them. These rovers were called Vikings.

The people of the other lands feared and hated these sea-rovers. When they saw the long, low boats of their foes sailing towards their shores, they drove their cattle and sheep into the forests and hid their gold and silver.

But the Northmen were clever at finding things. They took a great many cattle and much gold and silver away to their own land.

There was once a clever dog who saved his

A Viking ship

master's cows from the Northmen. King Olaf and his band of Vikings had come to Ireland. They had taken a great many cattle, and now they were driving the herd down to their boats.

In the herd were the cows of a poor man. He was very sad, for they were all he had, and he had no money to buy more. He feared his wife and children would starve. So he went to King Olaf, and told his story, and begged to have the cows back again.

The king was not an unkind man, and he

was sorry for the poor farmer.

"You may have your cows if you can pick them out of the herd at once," said he. "But I will not let you stop the march and waste the time of my men."

There were hundreds of cows in the herd. The poor man could not have found his own at once among the rest. But Vige, his clever dog, could do so.

The poor man tells his story.

The dog was sent into the herd of cattle. In a few moments, he had found one of his master's cows and had driven her out. Then he found another and another. Very soon the number, which the man had asked for, had been driven out of the herd.

Each of these cows was marked with the same mark, so the king knew that the dog had found the right ones. He was very much pleased. He offered a large sum of money for the clever animal.

The poor man would not sell his faithful dog, but he gave him to the king. And the king gave a gold ring to the man.

So clever Vige went away with the Northmen. He was treated well and lived long. The old books say that King Olaf was always very fond of this "best of dogs."

6

A Boy Who Became King

ONE day, long ago, three little boys were playing beside a lake in Norway. They were princes, and their brother was the good King Olaf.

The king came out to see what the children were doing. He saw that the two elder boys were building houses and barns and making fences around tiny fields. The youngest boy was floating chips of wood in a pool of water. This boy was only three years old. His name was Harald.

"What are those chips of wood?" asked the king.

"They are my warships," said little Harald.

The king smiled. "The time may come when you will have real warships," said he.

Then he called the two older boys to him. He asked them what they would like to have when they grew up.

"I should like to have land," said the eldest boy. "I should like that big piece of land, which stretches out into the lake. I would sow grain upon it."

"I should like to have cows," said the second boy. "I should like so many cows that, when they came down to the lake to drink, there would not be room for one more."

Then the king went to the pool where little Harald was sailing his ships.

"And what would you like to have, my little man?" asked he.

"I will have men to follow me and fight for me," said the child quickly. "I will have so many men that they will eat up at one meal all my brothers' grain and all the cows my brothers have.

The king smiled again when he heard these words. "That boy will be a king some day," said he. And he was right.

When the two elder boys became men, they grew grain and kept cows as they had wished to do. Their lives were quiet and happy.

But Harald became a king. He was the last of the sea-kings. He had many brave men to follow him and fight for him. They won many battles. But they did not eat up all the grain and cows of his brothers.

Some day you may read the story, which tells how King Harald came to England and fought his last battle there.

7

The Last English Lord

ONE of the greatest names in English history is that of William the Conqueror. He was not an Englishman at all, but he came over from Normandy, where he was duke, and made himself king of the English. The lords of England had a sad time then, for he took away their lands and houses and money, and he gave these things to his own Norman lords.

The English fought bravely, but they were not so strong as the Normans. One by one, the leaders were beaten, and most of them became King William's men.

The last English lord who fought against the king was very strong and brave. Men called him the Wake, because he was very

A Norman knight

watchful and wide-awake.

The Wake went to a wild, woody place and made a camp there. A few of his friends went with him. There were lakes and marshes, and soft muddy ground on all sides of the camp. The Norman soldiers with their heavy armor and their horses could not ride over this soft ground without sinking into the mud. And they did not know of the narrow, safe path, which led to the camp. It was hidden among the trees and rushes.

Soon many other Englishmen who hated the Normans went to the camp of the brave lord. At night, the Wake and his men went to the castles and farms of the Norman lords and took away cattle and food and money. They said they had a right to these things, because William had stolen them from the English lords.

The Normans tried to save their goods, but the bold Englishmen fought so fiercely that they were never beaten. When the fight was over, they went back to their camp among the marshes. The Normans could never catch them.

At last, King William thought of a way to reach the camp of the English robbers who gave so much trouble to his Normans. He dug ditches in the marsh to drain away the water. Then he began to make a firm high road of stones and turf across the wet ground.

When the Wake heard that the king himself was come out against him, he made up his mind to go and see what William was like.

The Wake dressed himself in plain clothes, got on his horse, and rode away to the king's castle. His horse had a rough coat. It looked like a farm horse, which would not be able to run very fast. But it was the fastest horse in England.

The Wake met a potter carrying his pots on the road to the castle. He bought the man's pots and changed clothes with him. Then he rode on.

He went into the kitchen of the castle and asked the servants to buy his pots. The Norman servants made fun of the English potter. They pulled his hair and trod on his toes.

At first, the Wake did not lose his temper. But he was very angry when a servant threw a dish-cloth into his face. He took up the cook's iron spit and began to fight.

King William heard the noise and sent some soldiers to the kitchen to see what was the matter. The soldiers took the potter to their master.

The Wake put on a stupid look when he went before the king. All men, except the king, thought he was a simple potter. But William was wise. He looked hard at his prisoner, and he saw that he was no common man.

"My friend," said he, "do you know the Wake? If so, tell him that I will be his friend and give him back his lands if he will promise to be my man."

But the potter did not answer the king. Then William went out to hunt. But he told his soldiers to keep the prisoner safe until he came back again.

As soon as the king was gone, a soldier got chains to put on the Wake. He told the prisoner to hold up his leg for the chain. But the bold Wake knocked the man down. Then he took the soldier's sword and ran out of the door.

The soldiers outside the castle tried to stop

him, but he drove them back with the sword. Then he jumped on his fast horse and galloped away.

But King William went on making his good road over the marshes. So at last, the Wake had to leave his hiding-place and become the king's man.

William treated him well and gave him back his lands. But the Norman lords did not forgive him. And after a time, twenty of them set upon him and killed him. The old story says that the brave Wake cut down sixteen of these lords before he was killed himself.

8

How Jerusalem Was Taken

YOU will remember the story of the poor children who tried to go to the War of the Cross. They wanted to fight for Jerusalem, where Christ died on the cross, and to take it away from the people who did not love and serve Him.

But they never reached that far-off city. Many of the poor little boys and girls died on the way. Others were taken by wicked men and sold as slaves.

But hundreds and thousands of men went to the Wars of the Cross. They came from many lands. Rich men and poor men, kings and lords, masters and servants, all wanted to fight for Jerusalem. Every man wore a cross

Soldiers of the Cross on the March

upon his coat or cloak. They were called the Soldiers of the Cross.

The men were stronger and wiser than the children. So they were able to go farther and to take care of themselves. Some of them reached Jerusalem and, at last, took it away from the Turks.

The Soldiers of the Cross were full of joy when they saw the towers of Jerusalem afar off. The horsemen got off their horses, and they and all the foot soldiers knelt down on the hard road. Then they prayed to God to help them to take the city.

These soldiers had many brave leaders. Tancred and Godfrey were two of the bravest and best. They led their men to the walls of Jerusalem and tried to take it at once. But they were driven back. Then they put up their tents and made a camp outside the city.

There were no guns in those days, but men had big engines of wood instead. The Soldiers of the Cross had taken no engines with them, so they had to make some.

No big trees grew near Jerusalem, for the ground was too dry and hard. But Tancred had seen some tall trees thirty miles away. He took some men to this place and cut down the trees and dragged them to the camp. This wood was made into three engines like tall towers.

In the dark of night, the three towers were drawn close to the walls of Jerusalem. And in the early morning, great stones and showers of arrows were thrown over the city walls by the soldiers upon the towers.

The Turks inside Jerusalem got on the city walls and shot arrows and threw heavy stones down on the army outside. They poured down boiling oil, too, and set fire to the tall towers of wood.

At first the Soldiers of the Cross put out these fires with vinegar. But soon every drop was gone. Water will not put out the flames of blazing oil. Before long, one of the towers was quite burned, and the others were much harmed.

Many soldiers were killed. Some were burned; others were crushed by the wood falling from the blazing towers. It seemed as if all would be lost. The Soldiers of the Cross began to lose heart.

Then Godfrey, lifting up his eyes, saw a horseman afar off on the Mount of Olives. The horseman wore shining armor. He held up a shield, and upon the shield was a red cross.

"See!" cried Godfrey. "It is Saint George who has come to help us. On, men! It is God's will that we win the city."

"It is God's will! It is God's will!" shouted the soldiers. And they dashed on fiercely.

Some jumped up on to the walls from the top of the burning towers. Some climbed over the walls with ladders. Some broke a hole in the wall. They poured like a flood into the city.

The Turks could not stand against these fierce, eager soldiers, who cried, "It is God's will," as they fought. They turned to fly, but many of them were killed. Jerusalem was taken.

Then Godfrey went to the grave where the body of Christ had been laid long years before. He knelt there and thanked God who had helped him to take the city. After him, the other leaders also knelt to thank God, and so did the soldiers.

Godfrey was made King of Jerusalem. But he would not put the crown on his head. He said it was not right for him to be crowned with gold in the city where Jesus Christ wore a crown of thorns upon his head.

He was a good man. He loved Jerusalem and ruled it well. But he did not live long.

Tancred and a band of brave soldiers stayed there for many years to fight the battles of the city.

9

Robin Hood

ONCE upon a time, a band of robbers lived in a big forest in England. They were brave and strong and merry men, and their leader was the bold Robin Hood.

Today we put people in prison if they rob others. But at that time, a great many things were done that we should not now think right.

Robin and his men were not really bad men. They liked a free life. So they lived in the big forest and shot the king's deer for food. When they wanted money or clothes, they stopped some rich man, who was riding through the forest, and took away his purse and his fine cloak and coat.

But they did not rob the poor. They were kind to them and often gave them food and money. And they never hurt a woman, or a child, or any person who was sick or sad. So the poor people loved Robin and his merry men, but the rich people hated them.

One day Robin heard that three men were to be hanged in a town, because they had killed one of the king's deer.

"I will not let this thing be done," said the bold chief of the forest band. So he dressed himself in beggar's clothes, that no man might know him, and went to the town. His men waited on a hill not far off.

Before long, the three men were brought out of prison. When the king's officer came to hang them, Robin spoke to him.

"Good sir!" said he. "Will you let me be hangman?"

Now the king's officer did not like the work of hanging a man, so he said:

"I will gladly let you be hangman, old beggar man. And you shall have the fine clothes and the money of the men when they are dead."

"No," said Robin, "I do not want their clothes and their money, but I will have three blasts on my horn." Then he blew three loud blasts on his horn. And when his men heard the sound, they ran down the hill into the town.

"Whose men are these?" asked the officer.

"They are mine, and I am the bold Robin Hood," said the beggar. "I have come to save these men."

The officer knew that he could not stop Robin from taking the prisoners away, for all the poor people in the town were ready to help the bold robber. So he set the three men free. And away they went into the forest to live with Robin and his merry men.

The rich people hated Robin Hood, because he robbed them. Many of them tried to kill him. But Robin knew the big forest well. He hid among the trees, now here, now there, and no man could find him.

At last, the king made up his mind to be Robin's friend and to ask the bold leader and his men to come to live at court. Then there would be no more robbing in the forest.

So the king went himself, with five of his lords, to look for Robin. They dressed themselves like monks, in long cloaks and hoods, so that the robbers might not know them.

Monks were men of peace; they did not fight. They helped the poor, and taught the children, and served in the churches. Robin

Shooting at the target

Hood did not fear monks, so he did not hide himself from them. They told him the wish of the king.

Robin loved his king, so he gave the visitors a good dinner. When dinner was over, a target or mark was set up under the trees, and the robbers shot at it with their bows and arrows.

If a man did not hit the target, he had a sharp box on the ear from Robin Hood. All this was done to amuse the monks. By and by, Robin himself missed the target. Then he asked the chief monk to box his ear. And the monk gave Robin so hard a blow that he fell to the ground.

He was much surprised to find that a man of peace had so strong an arm. He looked closely in the monk's face and saw that he was the king.

Then the robber-chief knelt down and asked the king to forgive him and his men.

"Surely I will forgive you, good Robin, if you will come and live with me," said the king.

So Robin went to live at the court. But he did not stay there long. He could not bear to live in a house and to be ruled by others. Soon he went back to the big forest, and there he lived for many years and was very happy.

At last, the bold Robin Hood became an old man. Then he fell ill. He went to the house of a woman to be cured, for he thought she was his friend.

But the woman was not a true friend. She wanted to please the rich people who hated Robin. She said she would take care of him and cure him, but, instead of doing so, she cut a vein in his arm. Then she went away and left him alone in a room to bleed to death.

She locked the door, so that he could not go out. And he was too weak and ill to jump out of the high window. But Robin had his good horn, and he blew three blasts upon that. The blasts were not loud, for he was too weak to blow hard.

One of his men heard the sound of the horn.

This man's name was Little John, and he dearly loved his master.

"I fear my master is near dead. He blows so softly," said Little John. He ran to the house of the woman, and broke down the door, and came to his master's side.

Robin was by this time weak and dying. Little John was very sad and angry to see him so.

"Let me burn this house and all in it," cried he. But his master would not let him do this.

"I have never hurt a woman while I lived, and I will not do so now that I am going to die," said he.

Then Robin asked for his bow and shot an arrow through the open window, out into the forest.

"Dig my grave at the place where you find that arrow," said he. "Lay a green sod under my head and another at my feet, and put my bent bow at my side that men may say when I am dead, 'There lies bold Robin Hood.'"

The arrow, which he had shot from the

window, was found under a tree. A grave was dug in that place. And the bold robber-chief was buried as he wished to be, in the big green forest which he loved so well.

Robin Hood was buried under a tree in the forest.

10

The Brave Men of Calais

CALAIS is in France. It is nearer to England than any other French town. This story tells how it was taken away from the French king by the English king, Edward the Third.

The people of Calais shut their gates when they saw the English soldiers coming to their town. King Edward knew that he could not break down the strong walls and gates. So he built a little town of huts outside the walls, and he and his men waited there.

They would not allow anyone to go inside or to come outside of the town. They meant to wait until the people of the town had eaten up all their food. Then they would have to open the gates, or they would starve.

At first, the people of Calais had good hope. They thought the French king would come to help them and drive away the English.

They gave a little food to each person every day and waited. But no help came. Before long, all the good food in the town was eaten, and the people became very hungry.

Then they ate their dogs and cats and horses. They even caught rats and ate them. But still no help came.

At last, when there was nothing more to eat, they knew that they could wait no longer. So they sent word to the English king that they would give up the town, if he would spare the lives of all the people in it.

But King Edward was angry, because he had been kept waiting so long. He would not spare all the people. This is what he said:

"If six of the best men in the town will come to me, with bare heads and bare feet, and with ropes round their necks, and the keys of the gates in their hands, I will do with them as I please, and the rest shall be saved."

The poor, starving people of Calais were very sad when they heard these words. Men and women cried, and nobody spoke a word. At last, one of the chief men stood up.

"My friends," said he, "it would be a sad thing to let so many people die of hunger. It will be better for six of us to die for the rest. I will give myself up to the English king, if five other men will go with me."

Soon five other brave men joined him. The little band said goodbye to their friends and went out of the town.

It was sad to see the six brave men. They were very thin and pale from want of food, and they were so weak that they could hardly walk.

Their heads and feet were bare, and there were ropes round their necks. Their leader had the keys of the gates in his hands. They knelt on the ground before the English king, and the leader spoke.

"Gentle king," said he, "here are we, six men of Calais. We are chief men and great merchants. We bring you the keys of our town and castle, and we give ourselves to you to save the rest of our people. We beg you in your kindness to have mercy on us."

The English soldiers wept to see and hear the brave men. But King Edward would not have pity upon them.

"This town shall be punished," said he. And he told the soldiers to cut off the heads of the six men.

Some of the English lords begged him to have mercy.

"Men call you a good king, but, if you do this thing, they will call you wicked and cruel," said they.

But the king would not hear them.

"Take the men away, and cut off their heads," he said once more.

So the soldiers took hold of the ropes, which were round the men's necks, and began to lead them away.

But the Queen of England had seen and heard all these things. Her heart was sad for the poor men, and she wept. Now she knelt down before the king, her husband.

"Gentle lord," said she, "I have sailed across the sea to see you, and you have given me no gift. Now, I beg you, if you love me, to give me the lives of these brave men."

For a long time, King Edward said no word. At last, he spoke.

"Lady," said he, "I wish you had not been here, for, when you beg so tenderly, I cannot say no to you. I give you the men. Do with them as you please."

It pleased the good queen to give food and clothes and money to the six brave men. Then she sent them back to their town. So they and all the people of Calais were saved.

There were ropes around their necks.

11
A Brave Man of Switzerland

THE people of the beautiful country of Switzerland have always loved to be free.

The kings of larger countries have often tried to take this little land for themselves. Sometimes they have beaten the Swiss people and have ruled over them for a short time.

But the Swiss could not bear to have these kings for their masters. They fought again and again until they drove away their foes. Many brave Swiss soldiers were killed in these battles, but they gladly died to make their country free.

At one time, a duke of Austria tried to make himself ruler of Switzerland. He marched into the land with a strong band of horsemen. His soldiers carried long spears and good shields of iron and steel. The Swiss men went out upon the mountains to meet their foes. They were a small band, and most of them were poor men. Some had short spears, but many had nothing but clubs of wood and round wooden shields.

The duke's soldiers laughed to see them.

"We will serve up all these men roast or boiled for thc duke's supper tonight," said they.

But they spoke too soon. They did not know how brave the Swiss soldiers were.

The horses of the duke's men were of no use upon the mountains. So the duke told his soldiers to get off their horses and to stand close together. Each man held his long spear before him, so that the sharp points of the spears made a wall of steel in front of the men.

The Swiss soldiers knelt down upon the ground and prayed to God to help them and to

"I will open a path of freedom."

have mercy upon those who might be killed. Then they rushed upon their foes. But they could not break through the wall of sharp spear points and could not reach their foes with their short spears and clubs.

Many of them were killed. The rest were driven back. Again they rushed forward, and again they were driven back, and many more were killed.

It seemed as if all would be lost.

Then a brave man thought of a way to break through the wall of steel. He was a poor countryman, and his name was Arnold.

"I will open a path of freedom, dear friends!" cried he. "Take care of my wife and children."

Then he rushed upon the foes with open arms. The duke's soldiers thought he must be mad to do such a thing. But they did not know his plan.

When he reached the wall of spears, Arnold clasped as many of the sharp points as he could reach in his arms and pressed them all at once to his breast. By doing this, he made a gap in the wall.

The rest of the Swiss soldiers were close behind him. As the brave Arnold fell to the

The death of Arnold

ground dead with many spear points fixed in his body, they rushed into the gap, which he had made.

Their short spears were of great use now that they were close to their foes. They fought fiercely. Many they stabbed; others they killed with the wooden clubs.

The duke's men were taken by surprise. They could not do much harm with their long spears now that the Swiss were so near them. They began to be afraid; soon they lost heart, and then they turned to fly.

But their servants had led the horses away, so they could not ride. They tried to run over the mountains, but the Swiss soldiers soon caught them. The duke and many of his men were killed, and the rest were made prisoners.

So Switzerland was saved by Arnold von Winkelried, the poor countryman, and the Swiss people did not lose their freedom. We may be sure that they took good care of the wife and children of their brave friend.

Every year on the day of the battle, they

come together in some parts of the country to show that they remember Arnold von Winkelried and are thankful to him.

12

The Lost Princes

IT is not always a good thing to be born a prince or a princess. Some princes and princesses have very unhappy lives.

About the time when Caxton began to print his book, there were two unhappy little princes in England. Their names were Edward and Richard, and they were sons of King Edward IV.

Their father died when they were quite young, and so Prince Edward should have been King of England. But the poor boys had a wicked uncle, who wanted to be king himself. So he sent the little princes to the strong Tower of London, out of the way.

He told the English people that he had done

The Tower of London

this, because he wished the boys to be safe, until Edward was old enough to wear the crown and rule the land. But this was not true. In his heart the wicked uncle was trying to find a way to get rid of the princes.

Edward and Richard were afraid of their uncle. He smiled and spoke kindly to them, but they knew that he did not love them. They were afraid too of the big dark place, to which he had sent them.

"I do not like the Tower," said Edward.

"I shall not sleep in quiet here," said Richard.

But their uncle laughed at their fears. "There is nothing here to be afraid of," said he.

One morning, when a lord went to waken the little princes, they were not to be found. Their bed was empty. Their uncle said he did not know where they were, and he pretended to be very sad, because they were lost.

The people thought he had killed the poor boys. Some said he sent two bad men to smother them with pillows when they were asleep. But most people were afraid of the wicked uncle, so nobody dared to punish him.

He took the crown for himself and ruled the land. But he did not live long. He was not a good king, and the people hated him. By and by, some of them fought with him, and he was killed.

Two hundred years after that, some men were at work in the Tower. They took up the stone floor at the foot of a stair. There they found a box, and in this box were the bones of two young boys. Most likely they were the bones of poor little Edward and Richard, who had been buried in that place.

Where the box was found

13

The Field of Cloth of Gold

WHEN kings and queens meet each other, there is often a fine show. Flags are waved, bands play gay music, and people wear rich and pretty clothes. Everybody tries to look happy.

Long ago there was a meeting between the English king, Henry VIII, and the French king, Francis I.

These two kings did not love one another in their hearts, but they tried to look as if they did. They wanted the people to think that they were very good friends and that there would be peace between the lands of England and France.

That is why they met. The meeting place

was a big plain in France, and a very grand show was made ready.

Palaces were built for the kings and queens, and tents were put up for their lords and ladies. The palaces were bright with gold and silver, and the tents were not made of canvas, but of silk and cloth of gold. So much gold was to be seen shining in the sun that the place was called the Field of Cloth of Gold.

It was a gay sight. There were sham castles and pretty gardens, and lions made of gold, and many other beautiful things. There were fountains running with wine instead of water. Every man was free to help himself to the wine.

This great show lasted for ten days. And every day, from morning till evening, there were feasts, and games, and sham fights.

The kings played games and had sham fights with each other, and with their lords. And the queens and their ladies looked on.

People went in crowds to see such grand doings. They watched the games and the fights and drank wine from the fountains. They saw the two kings sign their names on paper, and kiss one another, and promise to be friends. Then the people shouted and cheered.

Before the show was over, King Henry gave King Francis a golden collar, and King Francis gave King Henry a rich bracelet.

They kissed again when they said good-bye. The people thought they were true friends.

But in their hearts, the two kings did not love each other. Very soon the soldiers of England were sent to fight with the soldiers of France.

The grand doings at the Field of Cloth of Gold had been a show and nothing more. Such foolish things were often done in the old times.

14

How the Sea Won a Battle

HOLLAND is a very flat country; it has no mountains. Many hundred years ago, the sea washed over some of the lowest parts of the land. Then the people made great walls to keep the waves back. These walls are called dykes.

It was hard work to do this, and it cost much money. But it was worth doing. There are now green fields and houses and gardens full of flowers upon land, which was once at the bottom of the sea.

The city of Leyden stands in the midst of green and fruitful country, which has been saved from the sea. It is a fine city with good houses and wide streets. Upon a mound in

A dyke on the Dutch coast

the middle of the town, there is a high tower.

One summer, more than three hundred years ago, the people of Leyden were in a sad state. They were shut up in their city, and they had not enough food to eat.

Outside the city, there was a big army of soldiers. The soldiers came from Spain. Philip, King of Spain, was a cruel man, and he wanted to make all people worship God in his way. The people of Holland would not do this, so the king fought with them for seven long years.

Sometimes he beat them in battle. He killed many of the poor people and did very cruel things to hurt them. But he could not make them do what he wanted.

"As long as one man is left in the land, we will fight to be free, and we will worship God in our own way," said the people.

King Philip sent his soldiers to try to take Leyden. That is why the people were shut up in their city.

The soldiers could not get into Leyden, but they kept the people from coming out. They stopped anyone from taking grain, or meal, or meat, or any other kind of food into the town.

The soldiers knew that the food in the city would not last long. They thought that the people would open their gates and do as the king wished, as soon as the food was all eaten. If they did not do so, they would die of hunger.

But the soldiers of Spain did not know how brave the men and women of Holland were.

Sending letters from Leyden

The people of Leyden said they would rather starve than give up their city.

Before long, most of the food in Leyden was eaten. Then the people wrote letters to their friends in other cities of Holland. They told their friends of their sad state and asked for help.

They could not send men to carry these letters, for the soldiers would let nobody go out of the city. So they rolled the letters into tiny rolls and tied them under the wings of carrier-pigeons. The pigeons flew away, high above the heads of the soldiers, and carried the letters to the other cities.

The people of these cities caught the pigeons and read the letters. They were very sorry for their friends in Leyden. But they could not send food to them, for they had not enough men to beat the Spanish soldiers.

There was only one thing to be done. William the Silent, who led the men of Holland, thought of this thing. He was called William the Silent because he could keep a secret well. His plan was to make holes in the dykes and let the sea roll over the land, as it had done in the old times, before the walls were built.

The sea would do much harm to the fields, and houses, and gardens. But it would drive away their foes. The Spanish soldiers would have to run away, or they would be drowned.

Letters were written to the people of Leyden to tell them that the sea would bring them help. Pigeons carried these letters to the city.

The poor, hungry people were very glad to have this news. All their good food was now eaten. There was nothing left to eat but dogs, and cats, and rats. So they ate these and waited for help.

Every day, some of the starving men went to the top of the tower to see if the waves were rolling over the land. But the sea was long in coming.

Holes had been made in the dykes, but the water did not spread quickly over the country. The wind blew from off the land and kept the sea back. It seemed as if the poor people of Leyden would all be dead before help came.

But one night, there was a storm. The strong wind blew from off the sea. It drove the big waves fast over the land, till the flood reached the camp. Then at last, the Spanish soldiers ran away in great fear.

Very soon, ships full of good food sailed over the flooded land to the city of Leyden. The brave people were saved.

15
Sir Philip Sidney

MORE than four hundred years ago, there lived in England a nobleman named Sir Philip Sidney. He was a very wise man, so wise, indeed, that his queen often called on him to advise her about ruling her kingdom. He was a poet, too, and he was also a good soldier. He was so brave and so kind that all who knew him loved him. Almost everyone called him the darling of the court, and even the queen spoke of him as the jewel of her kingdom.

At this time, a war was being fought in Holland against the king of Spain. Now Queen Elizabeth of England was not on friendly terms with the king of Spain. She wanted to help the Dutch drive him from

Sir Philip giving water to the dying man

their country, so she sent an army into Holland. Among the soldiers who went with this army was Sir Philip Sidney.

In one of the battles of this war, Sir Philip's horse was shot from under him. Shells were flying all about him, but he was not afraid. He even did not want to leave the battlefield.

"Another horse!" he cried, and went on fighting.

But before long, a musket ball hit him in the leg, and he fell to the ground. He had been wounded very badly and was suffering great pain. His throat became parched with fever. Nothing could help him so much as a drink of water, but there was no water to be had just then.

When the fight was over, some of his friends came to carry him from the battlefield. The wounded man called for a drink, but not one of these soldiers had any water to offer him.

At last, one of his servants, who had heard his cry, came running to him with a small bottle of water.

Sir Philip smiled as he lifted the bottle to his lips. But just then his eyes fell upon a dying soldier lying near him. The poor man was so weak he could not speak, and he looked longingly at the bottle of water.

Sir Philip saw this look. Without tasting the water, he said to his servant, "Here, give the water to that man. His need is greater than mine." The servant gave the water to the dying man. Then he turned to help carry his master from the field.

Soon afterward, Sir Philip died of his wound. He never saw his native land again, but his body was taken back to England.

The people of England were very sad over the death of this brave soldier. All mourned for him, and all felt that they had lost a dear friend. Even today, the English people remember him as one of the bravest, kindest, and best men their country ever knew.

16
The Great Armada

GREAT Britain is an island. There is sea all round it, so that its foes would have to come across the sea in ships to reach the land. Many of the battles of Great Britain have been fought upon the sea.

There was a great sea fight in the days of Queen Elizabeth. The king of Spain hated Elizabeth. He made up his mind to fight with the English and to try to get the crown of England for himself.

So he got a fleet of strong warships ready and filled them with soldiers and sailors. He called his fleet of ships the Great Armada. He felt sure the English ships could not beat them. He meant to do great things.

Elizabeth heard what the king of Spain was doing. But she was not afraid, for, though she had not many ships or soldiers, she trusted her people. She called every man to come to help his country.

Almost every man came. Some said they would fight; some gave money and guns and horses; others built ships. Soon all was ready.

Men stood upon the hilltops near the sea to watch for the Spanish ships. Bonfires were made ready, and, as soon as the ships were seen, the fires were to be lighted. When the men saw the blazing fires, they would know that it was time to go out and fight.

It was on a fine, summer afternoon that the watchers on the hills saw the Great Armada coming. The Spanish ships were very big. They were as high as towers, and there were a great many of them. Very fine they looked as they came sailing on.

The bonfires were soon lighted on the English hills, and men ran quickly to the shore and to their ships.

The Game of Bowls

Some great English captains were playing a game of bowls on a green near the sea. A few of these captains started at once for their ships. But Drake, the greatest man of them all, called them back.

"There will be plenty of time to finish our game, and to beat the Spaniards too," said he,

So the game was played out. When it was ended, the great captains went on board their ships and sailed away.

That was the quiet way in which Drake and

his men went out to meet the Great Armada of Spain.

Queen Elizabeth had not nearly so many ships as the King of Spain. And her ships were small.

The Spanish captains laughed at them. They thought their big ships with their heavy guns would soon blow the little English ships to pieces or sink them. They sailed on, firing their guns as they went.

But the guns were so high up on the big ships that most of the shots passed right over the little English ships without touching them.

The English ships were not fine to look at, but they could move very quickly, because they were small and light. The big Spanish ships moved slowly.

The English captains fired at them and made holes in the sides of many of them. Some sank, while others had to stop and were taken by the English.

The Spanish captains could not sail away

from the fast, little English ships, and they could not catch them. So at last, they stopped near the shore and waited for other ships and soldiers that were coming to help them.

But the English found a good way of driving them out to sea. They filled eight of their own ships with things, which burn well and quickly. One night, after dark, a few men steered these ships close to the Armada. Then they set them on fire and rowed away quickly in their little boats.

There was a great blaze in the dark night. The Spaniards were much afraid that the burning ships would set their own on fire. So they cut their ropes and sailed away. The English ships

One of the Armada medals

sailed after them and fired at them.

Then a storm came on. The Armada was in a sad state. Some of the ships were taken by the English, and some were sunk by the storm.

After a time, the English captains stopped and went back. But the Spaniards sailed on, hoping to get back to their own land by another way. But it was not a safe way, for the waves were wild and the wind was strong.

Many of the ships were driven on the sharp rocks, and the men in them were drowned. Only a few of the ships ever reached home again.

The King of Spain was very sad at the loss of his fine ships and brave men. For a long time, he did not speak. But Queen Elizabeth and her people were very glad. She had many medals made, and on the medals these words were written in Latin: "God blew with his winds, and they were scattered." Some of these medals may still be seen.

17

How a King Stopped a Fight

WE think it right for a man to fight for his country. But it is not right to fight for small reasons.

In old days, there was too much fighting. Men fought for all sorts of small and foolish reasons. If one man was rude to another, there was a fight. If two men could not agree, they had to fight before they could settle their quarrel.

They fought about their houses and their wives, their dogs and their horses, their drink and their food. There was no end to it. Very often a man was killed in these fights, and many lives were lost in this way. It was very sad.

A wise king of Sweden made up his mind to stop these foolish fights among his soldiers.

His name was Gustavus.

One day, he heard that two of his officers had had a quarrel and were going to fight.

"Very well," said the king, "I will go to see that fight."

At the time fixed, the king went down to the field where the fight was to be. He took with him some soldiers and the headsman. The headsman was the man who cut off the heads of prisoners who had to die.

The two officers were already on the field, and some of their friends were with them. The king looked quietly at the officers. "Begin your fight, gentlemen," said he, "and go on fighting until one of you is killed."

Then he spoke to the headsman, who stood beside him, and said: "As soon as one of these officers has been killed in the fight, you are to cut off the head of the other one."

These words of the king stopped that fight, for neither of the officers wanted to have his head cut off.

After that time, the soldiers of Gustavus

kept their swords for battle and left off fighting with one another. It was useless for a man to win a fight, if he was sure to lose his head as soon as the fight was over.

A statue of Gustavus Adolphus at Stockholm, Sweden

18
A Shipwreck Which
Brought Good Fortune

A SHIPWRECK often brings bad fortune. The ship may be lost or broken, so that it is of no more use, and sometimes the people in it are drowned.

But there was once a shipwreck, which brought good fortune. The ship that was wrecked was going from Holland to India, and there were many Dutchmen on board.

It took a long time to go to India in those days. Long before the journey came to an end, the fruit and vegetables and fresh meat on the ships were all eaten. Then the sailors had to eat salt meat and dry biscuits.

Sometimes the drinking water turned bad. Then the sailors often became ill. People cannot keep well if they do not have plenty of good food to eat and fresh water to drink.

Sometimes captains stopped their ships for a short time near the coast of South Africa. They sent men in little boats to the land to fill the casks of the ship with fresh water and to buy meat from the people who lived there.

The ship full of Dutchmen, which was going to India, stopped in this way at a part of the sea called Table Bay. While it was there, a storm came on, and in the storm the ship was driven on the beach. It was so much broken that it was of no more use. But all the people were saved, and they were able to save their goods out of the ship.

The poor men looked at the wild land around them. They saw mountains and trees and wide plains where grass grew. There were no towns, or roads, or railways, or cornfields, or gardens. At night, they heard the wild beasts roar.

The Dutchmen found a stream of fresh water not far away. It is good to live near fresh water, so they cut down some trees and built huts upon the bank of the stream. Then they made a high wall of earth to shelter their huts and keep off the wild beasts.

This was their new home. They hoped that a ship would soon pass by and take them back to their own land.

There were some seeds among the things that were saved from the wrecked ship. The Dutchmen made a garden on the bank of the stream and planted these seeds. The rain and the sun made them grow very fast, and soon there were many nice vegetables in the garden.

But before this time, a party of black men had come to the place. They had many sheep and cattle. They drove their beasts from one place to another to find fresh grass for them to eat.

They sold sheep and cattle to the white men. They worked for them, too, and helped them to drive away the wild beasts.

The Dutchmen paid the black men with

knives, and clothes, and other useful things from the ship. They now had fresh water and meat and green food. They began to find their new home a pleasant place.

By and by, a ship passed that way and took the Dutchmen back to their own land. They told the people of Holland that South Africa was a good place to live in. Before long, another ship full of Dutchmen sailed to that country.

These men planted more gardens and grew fruit and vegetables. They kept sheep and cattle, too, upon the grassy plains. They sold

Where the laws are made at Capetown

these things to the Dutch sailors who passed that way in ships.

Then they built a hospital, where sick men from the ships could be taken care of until they were better.

By and by, the Dutchmen of South Africa began to grow rich. Then they built houses instead of huts and made big farms instead of gardens.

The land became a good place to live in. People from England and from other countries sailed across the sea to make their homes there.

South Africa is a rich country with big towns and good roads and railways, and fruitful farms and gardens. Gold and diamonds are found in some places.

Englishmen and Dutchmen live there together and make one nation.

A fine city called Capetown stands on the bank of the stream near the place where the first garden was made by the Dutchmen who were saved from the wreck.

We must not forget that it was these men who began to turn this land into a prosperous country.

19
A Great Sea Fight

VERY early one morning, a great many ships were sailing on the sea near the coast of Spain. They were the warships of France and Spain, and they were looking for the British warships. The British ships were waiting for them not far off.

It was more than a hundred years ago. The great French soldier Napoleon had won battles in many lands. Now he had made up his mind to bring a big army of soldiers to England to beat the British.

You may be sure that the British people did not mean to let him do that if they could help it. They sent out their warships to stop him. That is why they were waiting.

Lord Nelson's flagship, the Victory

The British had not nearly so many ships as their foes. But their leader was the best seaman in the world; his name was Nelson.

It was the same Nelson who said, when he was a little boy, "I never saw fear." Nelson never did see fear; he was always brave. His sailors loved him. "Our Nelson is as brave as a lion and as gentle as a lamb," said they.

On that day, when the French and Spanish ships came near, Nelson sent a last message to all his men. These were the words of the message: "England expects that every man will do his duty." The men cheered when they heard it.

Then the battle began. It was a fierce fight. The French and Spanish seamen were brave, but they had no chance against Nelson and his men. The British were fighting to save their land and their homes, and they loved their leader. They liked better to die than to be beaten. Every man did his best.

Before the fight was over, many of the warships of the foes had been taken. The great Napoleon was beaten. He would never be able to bring his soldiers across the sea to England.

There was great joy in England. But the people were sad, too, for their brave leader was dead. Nelson had been shot in the battle. Yet he lived long enough to hear that the battle was won; and he died happy, because he had saved his country.

"Thank God, I have done my duty." These were the last words he spoke.

20
Beaten by Ice and Snow

You have read of the boy Napoleon and of the games of soldiers he played with his school-fellows in the snow.

When Napoleon grew to be a man, he was a great soldier. He led the soldiers of France to battle with the soldiers of other lands and beat them. After he had beaten them, he made them fight for him.

He liked fighting more than he liked anything else. If he could win a battle, he did not care how many of his men were killed.

Napoleon went from land to land, fighting and winning battles for France. The people of other lands hated and feared him, but there came a time when this great soldier was beaten.

He led a great army to the far-off land of Russia. There were thousands and thousands of soldiers in that army. It was called the Grand Army.

The soldiers came from many lands. Some of them did not want to fight with the people of Russia. But they had to; Napoleon would have shot those who tried to run away.

Russia is a very big country. It is very cold there in winter. Winter was coming on, when the Grand Army marched through the land.

The French leader did not take much food for his men. He told them to steal food from the Russian houses and farms as they marched on.

But the way led through forests and wild land, and there were not many houses or farms where food could be got.

Before long, the men became tired and

Napoleon

hungry, but Napoleon cheered them on.

"When you reach the big city of Moscow," said he, "there will be plenty of food and clothes and money for you."

So the tired soldiers marched on, thinking of the good things they would have when they got to Moscow.

The people of Russia were ready for their foes. They had not so many soldiers as Napoleon, but men came from the castles, and the fields, and the shops, to fight for their country. They made a big army, but it was not so large as the Grand Army.

The Russians tried to stop the French from getting to Moscow. They fought a battle with them on the banks of a river, but they could not stop the great Napoleon. At last, they had to go away and leave the road to Moscow open.

Then the tired and hungry French soldiers marched on. They pushed into the fine old city. Now they hoped to have good food, and warm clothes, and houses to rest in.

But the houses were empty, and the streets were empty, and the shops were empty. No food was to be found. The people of Moscow had taken all the food and gone away from the city.

How disappointed the French soldiers were! Napoleon was more disappointed than any of his men. They went into the empty houses to sleep.

Then in the night, the Russians came back to the city and sct the houses on fire. Soon the whole city was in a blaze, houses fell, and the streets were blocked with burning wood.

The French soldiers could not stay there. Tired and hungry, they had to march back again; and a very sad march it was.

Winter had come. Snow fell thick, and the icy ground was as hard as iron. It was bitterly cold.

Some of the tired men could go no farther and fell down and died. Others died of hunger. At night, watch-fires were lighted, and the men lay down beside them to sleep. When morning came, many of the men did not get up. They were frozen.

Napoleon got into his carriage and drove away. He was selfish; he did not care about his poor men, now that there were no battles to win. But a few brave officers tried to cheer the soldiers and help them on their way.

They had nothing to eat or drink, so the horses were killed for food, and the snow melted for drink. Sometimes the Russian soldiers came to fight with the poor, tired French soldiers. The Russians could beat them easily now, and thousands of the French were killed.

Only a few sad and weary men reached their homes again. They were all that was left of the Grand Army.

21

The Men of the Sarah Sands

It is not only in battles that men can be brave. A great many brave deeds have been done on ships at sea in times of peace.

Not so very long ago, a ship called the Sarah Sands went out to sea. Three hundred British soldiers and their wives and children sailed in this ship. They were going to India. There were stores, too, in the Sarah Sands, and a cabin full of casks of gunpowder.

One day, when the ship was not far from land, there was a cry of "Fire!" Some of the stores were on fire. The sailors poured water on the flames, but they could not put them out.

Then the leader of the soldiers told his men

They threw the casks into the sea.

to throw the casks of gunpowder into the sea. This must be done quickly, for, if the fire reached the powder, the ship would be blown to pieces.

It was not a safe thing to do. The flames were very near the cabin, and at any moment a spark might reach it. But the brave soldiers did their duty. Very soon the casks were thrown into the sea. One cask blew up and broke a hole in the ship, but nobody was hurt.

The fire went on spreading, till half the ship was ablaze. The women and children were put into the small boats for safety, but the men stayed on the ship and tried to save it. For two days, they worked hard, and they won at last. The fire was put out.

But the poor people were not yet safe. Now came another danger, for the wind rose and the sea became rough. The ship was already almost a wreck. Great holes had been burned in it, and it seemed as if the wild waves would break it to pieces.

But the soldiers and sailors did not lose heart. They had fought the fire; now they fought the sea. They stopped the holes with sails and blankets, and they passed a chain under the ship to keep it from breaking up.

At last, the sea grew calm, and the captain was able to steer his ship to land. Every person was saved. But, if each man had not done his duty, hundreds of lives would have been lost.

In an old church in an English city, some

faded flags are hanging. They belong to the soldiers who fought the fire on the Sarah Sands. They are kept there to remind the people of the work of these brave men.

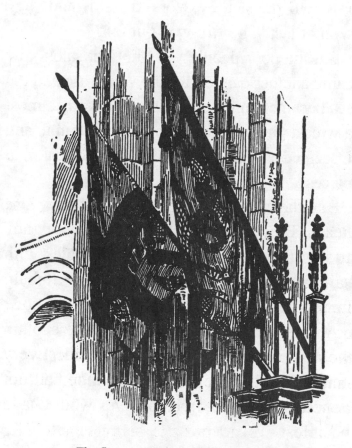

The flags carried on the Sarah Sands *now hang in Norwich Cathedral.*

22

The Penny Post in Britain

THE postman brings our letters to the door every day. A letter goes a long way for a few English pennies. It travels very quickly in a mail train.

A hundred years ago, people had to pay one or two shillings (24 to 48 cents) for a letter, and it took a long time to reach the end of its journey. There were no trains in those days. Letters were carried by postboys who rode on horses. They could not go very fast, for the roads were bad. When better roads were made, mail coaches carried the letters between the big towns.

There were no postage stamps then. The postman had to collect the money for the

A mail coach in the old days

letters before he gave them up.

One day, a young man named Rowland Hill saw a postman go to a cottage with a letter. A girl came out of the cottage and looked at it. But she did not open it; she gave it back to the postman.

The young man felt sorry for her. He thought she had no money to pay for the letter, so he paid the postman and gave it to her.

When the postman was gone, the girl told

Rowland Hill that it was a pity he had done so, for there was nothing written in the letter. Her brother was in London. Both he and she were poor, and they had no money for letters. So he sent a plain sheet of paper by post, now and then, to show her that he was well.

When Rowland Hill heard this story, he began to think. And this is what he thought: "Poor people would be happier if postage was cheaper, for they could then write more letters to their friends. It would cost the Post Office no more money to send many letters for a penny each than to send few letters for one or two shillings each. If stamps were stuck upon the letters to

The General Post Office, London

pay for them, the postman would not have to waste his time by stopping at the houses to collect pennies for the letters."

At first, people laughed at these thoughts of Rowland Hill. They said a letter could not be carried for a penny. But, by and by, they began to think as he did.

Now we know that he was quite right. A letter is taken to any part of the world for pennies. People send so many letters that the Post Office is much richer than it was in the old days, when only a few letters were sent at a much higher rate.

Index with Pronuciation Guide
PROUNUNCIATION KEY

This list of the most important names in the book tells you on what page you may find each name and how to sound those you may not know.

Sound	In These Words	Sound	In These Words
a	map, pat	o	pot, stop
ā	ate, face	ō	over, go
â	care, pair	ô	order, all
ä	far, farther		
		u	cut, butter
e	pet, west, head		
ē	we, meet	oi	boil, voice
		ou	shout, house
i	in, bit		
ī	nice, tiger	o͝o	pull, put
		o͞o	rule, move, use, music

ə represents:

a	in about	o	in lemon
e	in token	i	in happily
	u	in circus	

Index

F

G

H

I

J

L

M

N

O

R

S

Index